05

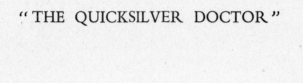

"THE QUICKSILVER DOCTOR"

THE QUICKSILVER DOCTOR

THE LIFE AND TIMES OF
THOMAS DOVER
PHYSICIAN AND ADVENTURER

BY

KENNETH DEWHURST

BRISTOL: JOHN WRIGHT & SONS LTD.

1957

PRINTED BY
JOHN WRIGHT & SONS LTD.
AT THE STONEBRIDGE PRESS
BATH ROAD, BRISTOL 4

IN MEMORIAM
MATRIS MEAE

PREFACE

THE bare facts of Thomas Dover's life are not without interest
or importance. The powder which still bears his name has
been a household remedy for two centuries, and the voyage
round the world, in which he played a conspicuous part, was
the most successful privateering expedition in British maritime
history. It was during this voyage that Dover rescued
Alexander Selkirk who, it is said, provided Defoe with the
germ of truth which he swelled into the great romance of
Robinson Crusoe. He met many famous contemporaries,
amongst whom were Dr. Thomas Sydenham, Captain
William Dampier, Sir Hans Sloane, Captain Woodes Rogers,
and possibly Robert Harley, Earl of Oxford and
Mortimer.

It is, therefore, not surprising to find that Dover's eventful
life has received the attention of many writers, and over a
score of articles have appeared in various medical journals
together with many more in the lay press. The earliest
contributors were two eminent medical historians : Sir
Norman Moore in the *Dictionary of National Biography*,[1] and
Sir William Osler's paper which first appeared in the *Bulletin
of the Johns Hopkins Hospital* of 1896,[2] and was later reprinted
in his *Alabama Student* (1926).[3] Then came three outstanding
papers by the late Professor J. A. Nixon[4] of Bristol wherein
many new details of Dover's early life were revealed. I am
most grateful to his widow for giving me reprints of her
husband's work. More recently Dr. D. N. Phear[5] has

---

[1] Sir NORMAN MOORE, *Dictionary of National Biography*, 1888, **15**, 382.
London : Smith and Elder.

[2] Sir WILLIAM OSLER, *Bull. Johns Hopk. Hosp.*, 1896, **7**, 1.

[3] Sir WILLIAM OSLER, *An Alabama Student, and other Biographical Essays*,
1926, 19. London : Oxford University Press.

[4] J. A. NIXON, *Bristol Med.-Chir. J.*, 1909, **27**, 31. *Proc. R. Soc. Med.*,
1912-3, *Sect. Hist.*, **6**, 233. *Brit. med. J.*, 1913, **1**, 619.

[5] D. N. PHEAR, *J. Hist. Med.*, 1954, **9**, 139.

brought new facts to light; but the majority of other writers have been content, for the most part, to rehash the work of these pioneers, or to distort the more colourful aspects of Dover's life.

But in spite of much research, many aspects of Dover's life are still unknown. He lived a long time ago. Since his undergraduate days the records of Magdalen Hall, Oxford, have perished in a college fire, and St. Peter's Hospital, Bristol, where Dover was the first honorary physician, was destroyed by enemy action in the late war.

Nevertheless, I can claim that this book does contain much new material, for which I am indebted to a number of people who have kindly aided my research. Most of them were long-suffering librarians who patiently ransacked their archives and answered my queries. In particular I would like to thank Mr. H. M. Nixon, Assistant Keeper at the British Museum; Mr. W. R. Le Fanu, Librarian of the Royal College of Surgeons of England; Sir Harold Boldero, Registrar, and Mr. L. M. Payne, Assistant Librarian, of the Royal College of Physicians; Dr. E. Ashworth Underwood of the Wellcome Historical Medical Museum; Miss Elizabeth Ralph, Assistant Archivist to the City of Bristol; and Mrs. Josephine Lyons, who lent me her copy of Dover's *The Ancient Physician's Legacy*. I am also indebted to Dr. I. A. B. Cathie, Squire of Barton-on-the-Heath, for showing me around Dover's birthplace, and to the President and Fellows of Corpus Christi College, Oxford, for a grant from the Charles Plummer Fund. Dr. H. M. Sinclair, Dr. A. T. H. Robb-Smith, and Dr. John Pearson have read the manuscript and I am grateful for their suggestions. Mr. L. G. Owens of Messrs. John Wright & Sons, the publishers, has been most helpful in preparing the book for the press. Mrs. D. E. M. Birtles has typed the manuscript, and the proofs have been checked by Mr. Edward Grant. Finally, I would particularly like to thank Lieut.-General Sir William P. MacArthur, K.C.B., D.S.O., O.B.E., M.D., physician, soldier, and man of letters, whose counsel I have constantly sought.

Dover's story is long and varied. It is regrettable that, even after intense research, many details of his life are still unknown; and hence, in following him down the devious by-ways of his life I may well have transgressed an important maxim of biography, as well as of tactics, in presenting a lengthy front with but light defence in depth. Even after much background reading I cannot claim to be an expert on maritime affairs, or a trained historian. There may, therefore, be errors of historical selection, of misconception, or of plain ignorance; but I have constantly strived to allow Thomas Dover to be his own interpreter, and thereby I hope to have avoided the cardinal errors of prejudice and lack of true objectivity.

March, 1957   K. D.

CONTENTS

LIST OF PLATES

CHAPTER I

THE DOVER FAMILY

Now be it written, Lo ! this was the man,
DOVER, that first these Noble Sports began,
Lads of the Hills, and Lasses of the Vale,
In many a Song, and many a merry Tale
Shall mention thee ; and having leave to play,
Unto thy name shall make a Holiday.

ANNALIA DUBRENSIA

BARTON-ON-THE-HEATH is a typical Cotswold village at the southern extremity of Warwickshire, where that county merges with Gloucestershire, Oxfordshire, and Worcestershire. Succeeding centuries have only slightly modified the outward aspect of the village : mechanization is a visible emblem of the twentieth century ; urbanization has reduced the population ; an aerodrome now stands about a mile from the village on the road to Moreton-in-Marsh ; but around the age-old triad of manor house, church, and inn are the rich pastures which still support its inhabitants. Just a few paces north of the village green stands a large mullion-windowed farmhouse built of Cotswold stone which the weathering of centuries has mellowed to a restful hue. It was here that Thomas Dover, the younger son of John Dover, gentleman-farmer and sometime Royalist Captain of Horse, was born in 1662, two years after the Restoration.

He was destined for many varied and turbulent adventures far from the pastoral simplicity of his native Cotswolds. As one of the commanders of a privateering voyage he circumnavigated the globe, and took by storm the city of Guayaquil, chief port of Ecuador : he was also the man who rescued Alexander Selkirk (Defoe's ' Robinson Crusoe ') from the island of Juan Fernandez. When a London physician, he was known as the "Quicksilver Doctor" on account of his liberal advocacy of crude mercury—a form of treatment which led to heated disputation amongst medical men for half a century after his death. As the author of one of the most controversial medical books of the eighteenth century, he was involved in disputes with both the College of Physicians and the Company of Apothecaries.

Though often the central figure of heated controversy the vagaries of time are such that his niche in posterity is a powder label—'Dover's Powder'—prescribed throughout the centuries with slight knowledge of the swashbuckling man of action with whose name this household remedy is still linked.

The Dovers were a versatile family, many of whom were notable personalities in their day and generation. They originated from Norfolk. Robert Dover, the grandfather of Thomas, came from Great Ellingham; and after reading law at Gray's Inn, began practising at Barton-on-the-Heath, where he rapidly gained a reputation as a peace-loving lawyer, "who never tried but two causes, always made up the difference".[1] He also achieved great local popularity as the originator of the "Cotswold Games", which took place annually in the parish of Weston-sub-Edge in Gloucestershire, where the arena is still known as Dover's Hill. It lies about a mile from Weston, equidistant from the old market town of Chipping Campden, and in those days consisted of five hundred acres of unenclosed land which provided an excellent spot for their "harmlesse mirth and jollitie".[2] Anthony Wood gives the following account of the origin of the Cotswold Games :—

The said games were begun, and continued at a certain time in the year for forty years by one Robert Dover, an attorney of Barton-on-the-Heath in Warwickshire, son of John Dover of Norfolk, who being full of activity and of a generous, free and public spirit, did with leave from King James I select a place on Cotswold Hills in Gloucestershire, whereon these games should be acted. Endimion Porter Esq., a native of that county, and a servant to that King, and a person also of a most generous spirit, did, to encourage Dover, give him some of the King's old cloaths, with a hat

[1] *Annalia Dubrensia*, 1878, 4. Ed. E. R. Vyvyan.
[2] *Ibid.*, 5.

and feather and ruff, purposely to grace him, and consequently the
solemnity. Dover was constantly there in person well mounted and
accoutred, and was the chief Director and manager of these games frequented by the nobility and gentry (some of whom came sixty miles to
see them) even till the rascally rebellion was begun by the presbyterians,
which gave a stop to their proceedings, and spoiled all that was generous
and ingenious elsewhere.[1]

The games revived again after the Commonwealth, and
were carried on with great spirit until 1846, after which time,
instead of being (as was originally intended) decorously
conducted sports after the manner of the Olympic Games,
these gatherings degenerated into rowdy hooliganism, and
following frequent appeals by the local inhabitants, they were
prohibited by an Act of Parliament in 1852. One of the last
eye-witness accounts of the games appears in the *Mirror* :

At the southern extremity of the hill is a thick wood, called Weston
Park ; under the shade of the trees on the borders of this wood the booths
are built, and the principal sports are carried on (on the Thursday and
Friday in Whitsun week). They consist of single stick (in Gloucestershire
called backsword), wrestling, running, jingling, morris dancing and other
sports of minor importance. On Friday the sports conclude with a horse
race for fifty pounds. There are generally about twelve couples who
play at backsword, the prize is a guinea each couple, eighteen shillings go
to the victor, and three shillings to the vanquished. The prize for wrestling is a handsome silver cup. . . . I believe these sports are partly supported by subscription and partly by a sum of money that was bequeathed
for the purpose. That they are very ancient may be adduced from its
being asserted in an old work which I have read, that the immortal Shakespeare was sometimes a spectator of these games (being celebrated about
ten miles from the place of his nativity), and that many of the Scenes of his
comedies were taken from Dover's meetings, especially the wrestling
scene in *As You Like It*.[2]

Indeed, it is highly likely that William Shakespeare frequented Dover's Cotswold Games as he refers to them again in
The Merry Wives of Windsor, when Justice Shallow asks :
" How does your fallow greyhound, sir ? I heard say he was
outrun on Cotsall. " There was every reason for Shakespeare's
visits to Barton-on-the-Heath, as his relatives the Lamberts
lived there. Edmund Lambert's wife was Joan Arden, sister

[1] ANTHONY WOOD, *Athenæ Oxonienses*, 1813, 3rd ed., Vol. IV, 222.
Ed. Philip Bliss.
[2] *Mirror*, June 10th, 1826.

of Shakespeare's mother; thus when visiting these relatives Shakespeare may well have become acquainted with Robert Dover. Many lawyers and Shakespearian authorities, after noting the poet's familiarity with legal terms, have suggested that at some time during his life the poet worked with a lawyer. Although definite evidence is wanting, it is just possible that Shakespeare's legalisms were culled from his acquaintance with Robert Dover, whom he may have met, either through his relatives the Lamberts, or from their common friend Ben Jonson.

The Cotswold Games and their patron were celebrated in a collection of poems, published in 1636, called *Annalia Dubrensia*, written by thirty-three eminent poets, of whom the best known are Ben Jonson and Michael Drayton. It is quite evident that the contributors to *Annalia Dubrensia* greatly respected Robert Dover for his broad outlook, practical ability, and kindness of heart. He had ample means, and early in life gave up the practice of law to settle at Winchcombe, where he devoted his leisure to field sports and the organization of his annual games. In 1700 Dr. Thomas Dover caused another edition of *Annalia Dubrensia* to be reprinted, as he " thought it his duty to perpetuate the memory of that good man his grandfather ".

Robert Dover's wife was Sibilla, daughter of William Cole, Dean of Lincoln, and sometime President of Corpus Christi College, Oxford. Cole made quite a stir in his day as the central figure of an Oxford religious controversy. He was expelled from Corpus about 1553 soon after the accession of Queen Mary, and formed one of the band of English Protestants who composed a literary society around Peter Martyr at Strasbourg. With others, including Robert Horne, afterwards Bishop of Winchester, Cole lived in dire poverty at Zürich. During their exile they translated the *Geneva Bible*. When Elizabeth came to the throne, William Cole was appointed President of Corpus Christi College in spite of strong Catholic opposition. His fellow exile Horne became Bishop of Winchester and Visitor of that college. Strype gives an amusing account of Cole's installation as President. " As for Corpus Christi, the Queen appointed one Cole, a learned and good man, once an exile, to be president there. But the college would not admit him, and elected another named Harrison, who had before left the college out of an affection to the Popish religion. Insomuch that the Bishop of Winchester, the Visitor of that college, was fain to institute a visitation, and placed the said Cole by force in the said presidentship, breaking open the gates of the house which they had shut against him."[1]

His appointment proved anything but satisfactory for the college, which he defrauded and eventually brought into debt. Also Cole's relations with other members of the college were constantly strained, involving frequent appeals to the Visitor. It may be that as the first married President he found it necessary to resort to novel ways of providing for his family ; but it is clear from the absence of records that the administration of the college estates was chaotic, and he left a long legacy of disputes with the tenants for his successor. Eventually Cole was called to task by the Bishop of Winchester, and their meeting is described by Anthony Wood :—

As for Mr. Cole (who was the first married President that Corpus Christi College ever had) being settled in his place, acted so foully by defrauding the college and bringing it into debt (not to be recruited till Dr. Reynolds became President) that divers complaints were put up against him to the Bishop of Winchester, Visitor of that college. At length the said bishop, in one of his quinquennial visitations, took Mr. Cole to task, and, after long discourses on both sides, the bishop plainly told him, " Well, well, Mr. President, seeing it is so, you and the college must part without any more ado, and therefore see that you provide for yourself." Mr. Cole, therefore, being not able to say any more, fetcht a deep sigh and said, " What, my good lord, must I then eat mice at Zürich again? " Meaning that must he endure the same misery again that he did at Zürich, when he was an exile in Queen Mary's reign when he was forced to eat carrion to keep life and soul together. At which words the bishop being much terrified, for they work with him more than all his former oratory had done, said no more, but bid him be at rest and deal honestly with the college. So that though an end was for that time put to the business, yet means were afterwards found that he should resign his presidentship, for the Deanery of Lincoln.[2]

Robert Dover and Sibilla Cole had four children, two girls and two boys, of whom Robert died in infancy, and John, the

[1] JOHN STRYPE, Life of Archbishop Grindal, 1821, Bk. I, 190.
[2] ANTHONY WOOD, The History and Antiquities of the University of Oxford, 1796, Vol. II, Annals 166–167. Ed. J. Gutch.

younger son, born in 1614, was the father of Thomas Dover.
His wife, Elizabeth Vade, was a lady of good family descended
from Sir Anthony Keck, and related to the Tracys of
Stanway Hall. John Dover was a practical man. Though
unlettered, unpolished, and lacking in all social graces he was
a gentleman nevertheless; and a fair representative of the
class to which he belonged. During the Civil War he had
served with great distinction as a Captain of Horse under the
command of Prince Rupert; and after the King's defeat
retired to farm his lands at Barton. Captain John Dover had
three sons and five daughters : only two of the sons, John and
Thomas, lived to adult life.

John, who was nearly twenty years older than Thomas,
was of a versatile though somewhat whimsical nature. At
fifteen he matriculated at Magdalen College, Oxford, but
after four years' residence he left without taking a degree.
He then entered Gray's Inn, where in order to mitigate
the severity of his studies he wrote a tragedy in heroic verse.
" After I had read a sect or two in Littleton ", he writes,
" I then to divert myself took Cæsar's Commentaries, or
read the lives of my Roman Generalls out of Plutarch."[1]
John Dover was called to the Bar in 1672, and five years later
his play, *The Roman Generalls or the Distressed Ladies*, was
published and played in London. It earned him a minor
reputation as a dramatist, though judging from his account,
Anthony Wood does not seem unduly impressed with it :
" 'Tis a play in heroic verse and dedicated to Robert, Lord
Brook. The plot, as far as it concerns history, may be read
in Plutarch's Lives of Cæsar and Pompey. He hath written
one or two more plays, which are not yet printed."[2]

John Dover practised law at Banbury for about twelve
years, but tiring of his profession, he took holy orders, and
became Rector of Drayton. Whilst he was the incumbent of
Drayton a singular incident occurred there, which came to the
notice of contemporary historians. John Gistelow, a regular
church-goer, expressed his doubts about a further existence

---

[1] JOHN DOVER, *The Roman Generalls, or the Distressed Ladies*, 1677, 4.
[2] ANTHONY WOOD, *Athenæ Oxonienses*, 1813, 3rd ed., Vol. IV, 598.
Ed. Philip Bliss.

after death to another parishioner, Mrs. Cleaver. Whereupon she asked his reason for attending service so regularly. " Merely in compliance with Custom, and to look well in the eyes of the world ", was his reply.[1] At the same time he suggested to Mrs. Cleaver that, should he predecease her, then by some means or other he would inform her as to whether there was any such thing as an extracorporeal existence. Some four years later this gentleman died, and on the following day, when the deceased's son was viewing the body, he noticed that one of his father's hands lay across his breast. The son endeavoured to bring it down to the side, but was unable to move the limb. He then asked the undertaker whether both arms were originally placed by the side. He was assured that they were. The son made another attempt, and with all his strength, fixing his foot against the bed, tried to pull down the hand, but could not in the least stir it. It so happened that Mrs. Cleaver was in the house, so she was called. Immediately upon her taking hold of the hand, it fell down with the greatest ease to his side. The gentleman was duly buried by the Reverend John Dover, who added that the deceased had never expressed to him any scepticism regarding the immortality of the soul. Evidently John Dover was contented with his last calling : at all events he remained at Drayton until his death at the age of eighty-one.

Such were the ancestors of Thomas Dover, or at least that is all that we know about them. They were a curious mixture of clerics, soldiers, lawyers, and scholars ; and his boyhood in such a family is not difficult to imagine. Captain Dover would be busy for the most part with farming and field sports. There were tenants to supervise ; samples of grain to examine ; outbuildings and fences to be repaired ; and on market days bargains to be made with drovers and hop merchants over a tankard of ale. At that time the rotation of crops was imperfectly understood, and it was not then the custom to grow turnips in order to feed the cattle during the winter. Instead the beasts were slaughtered in great numbers during the autumn, and the meat salted and stored. When

---

[1] Rawlinson MSS., B.400, Bodleian Library.

old enough young Thomas would accompany his father around his lands. In the tradition of his grandfather he would be reared a sportsman and taught to ride, to breed and train hounds, to handle a sword, and to shoot with musket and pistol.

From childhood Thomas Dover would be surrounded by traces of the Civil War. He must often have fondled his father's old sword and holster; and around his home were many crumbling ruins that had once withstood the cannon of Cromwell and Fairfax. His father's stories of bygone battles would further kindle his imagination. The old cavalier would find his son an eager listener to his tales of Goring and Lunsford, of lesser skirmishes, of reconnoitring, and ambushing. But above all else young Thomas would never tire of listening to the details of how Prince Rupert's cavalry swooped on the Roundheads with all the vainglorious desperation of a heartfelt cause. At such times he could see (if only with the mind's eye) his father at the head of a troop of horse. He could visualize the vivid flash of colour and the glint of swords as they swept into attack; he could hear the mounting thunder of hoofs; could feel the pounding of his horse's heart-beats against his thighs; and could smell the pungent odour of powder mingling with steaming animal sweat.

Although no longer a dashing cavalry commander, Captain Dover was still an officer in the local militia. A large standing army had become a thing of the past, and a local militia officered by the squirearchy and bolstered by many of the old cavaliers now replaced a larger centralized force. The inefficiency of this small body of rustic soldiery brought forth the ridicule of Dryden in *Cymon and Iphigenia* :—

> The country rings around with loud alarms,
> And raw in fields the rude militia swarms;
> Mouths without hands, maintained at vast expense,
> In peace a charge, in war a weak defence.
> Stout once a month they march, a blustering band,
> And ever, but in time of need, at hand.
> This was the morn when, issuing on the guard,
> Drawn up in rank and file, they stood prepared
> Of seeing arms to make a short essay,
> Then hasten to be drunk, the business of the day.

During his boyhood Thomas was the only son at home and in a largely feminine household he would occupy a position of privilege with his father. Feminine aspirations were not encouraged amongst the daughters of seventeenth-century farmers, who regarded them as little more than auxiliary housekeepers. They stitched, spun, and cooked, brewed wine, and fed the ducks. In regular sequence they married and went their way. Sibilla and Sarah married whilst Thomas was still an infant; and later Mary married Samuel Hopkins, an apothecary who was to accompany Thomas Dover on his voyage round the world. Finally, when Thomas was still a schoolboy, Magdalene and Anne (then only fifteen) were married within a year of one another at St. Martin-in-the-Fields.

There is no doubt that Thomas was his father's favourite, as in his will Captain John Dover virtually disinherited his elder son, the cleric, who was only mentioned to the extent of five pounds " to buy him a mourning goune ".

Thomas Dover probably attended Chipping Campden Grammar School, an old foundation, and the nearest school to his home; here he must have been taught the elements of grammar and mathematics, a smattering of Greek, Latin, and the Scriptures. The routine of farm life would inevitably stimulate his interest in natural science; and probably first directed his thoughts to medicine as a profession. However, judging by his subsequent life, Thomas Dover was undoubtedly influenced by his father. Captain Dover set him an example of manliness, and instilled in him a lasting aptitude for practical affairs which was to prove more important in his future development than any knowledge gained from books.

When Thomas Dover was eighteen years of age it was decided that he should read medicine, and on December 1st, 1680 he became a commoner at Magdalen Hall, Oxford.

CHAPTER II

OXFORD AND CAMBRIDGE

To Oxenford the King has gone,
With all his mighty peers,
That hath in peace maintained us,
These five or six long years.

ANON.

MAGDALEN HALL owed its origin to Bishop Waynflete, who
first established this institution in 1485 as a grammar school
connected with Magdalen College. During the succeeding
two centuries the School gradually became the Hall; at first
it was dependent on Magdalen College for the election of the
Principal, but later in Dover's time it was virtually independent. For some years after the Civil War, Magdalen Hall
had been the stronghold of the Oxford Puritans; it was the
seminary of Thomas Sydenham, but in 1662, following the
election of Dr. James Hyde as Principal, the religious temper
of the Hall was completely reversed.

Hyde had formerly been a Fellow of Corpus Christi, until
that college deprived him of his fellowship when the
Parliamentary party arrived. During Cromwell's rule he had
created quite a stir in the University by being the only person
who had refused to take the oath of protestantism against
popery. At the Restoration his courageous action was
rewarded and he was appointed to the Chair of Medicine
which he held until his death in 1681, during Dover's second
year of residence. Dr. Hyde was not a particularly distinguished medical man, but his appointment resulted from his
firm religious convictions rather than from any outstanding
academic ability. His death precipitated a struggle between
the Fellows of Magdalen College (who nominated Francis
Smith) and the Chancellor of the University, represented by

Dr. William Levet, a former Fellow of Magdalen Hall, who was eventually elected Principal.

Thomas Dover resided at Magdalen Hall for six years, and then transferred to Caius College, Cambridge ; but personal details of his Oxford life are wanting, as the records of Magdalen Hall were destroyed by fire early in the nineteenth century. However, a fair idea of his University residence can be obtained from many notable authorities. The Oxford of Dover's day was undergoing a period of transition and instability, still bearing the influences of rebellion. The harsh austerity of the Commonwealth was followed by the laxity of the Restoration. Anti-puritan reaction was so widely manifest that whatever the canting Roundhead had treated with reverence was now openly ridiculed. But the pendulum had swung too far and lost its equilibrium amidst an outburst of shameless swaggering licentiousness, at once inelegant and inhuman. In the University there was corruption in high places. Fellowships were then sold, at Magdalen and New College—when they were not given by favour. Despite his strong Royalist sympathies, Anthony Wood in his diaries gives clear evidence of a general decline in learning and morals towards the end of the seventeenth century. There was a general relaxation of discipline with drunken masters, fellows, and undergraduates, amongst whom immorality, gambling, and brawling was rife. In contrast to later years it appears that even Balliol men had a reputation for heavy drinking—" There is, over against Balliol College, a dingy, horrid, scandalous ale-house, fit for none but draymen and tinkers, and such as, by going there, have made themselves equally scandalous. Here the Balliol men continually, and by perpetuall bibbing add art to their natural stupidity, to make themselves perfect sots."[1] Contemporary writers even suggest that " serious men hesitated to send their sons to the university lest their minds should be corrupted ".[2]

But dimly and unconsciously forces were awakening which were to unsettle the traditional foundations of learning.

[1] ANTHONY WOOD, The History and Antiquities of the University of Oxford, 1796, Vol. II, Annals 148. Ed. J. Gutch.
[2] Ibid., 154.

The supreme object of university teaching was still directed towards the training of churchmen to vindicate Church doctrine; but towards the end of the seventeenth century they were no longer exercising their former ascendancy. At first, almost imperceptibly, the influence of experimental science was beginning to ruffle the placid surface of clerical Oxford : for the seventeenth century marked the triumph of Baconian philosophy. Boyle, Harvey, Sydenham, Wren, and Willis were amongst the vanguard of Oxford pioneers whose work, based on experiment and deduction, had instituted a new approach to scientific problems, leaving many old theories derelict in their wake.

But it took some time before these new ideas became absorbed into the Oxford medical curriculum. The regulations for the degree of Bachelor of Medicine were meagre. A candidate had to be a Master of Arts, have spent three years reading medicine, and attended twice-weekly lectures on Hippocrates and Galen by the Regius Professor. The course of study which Thomas Dover would have to follow was primarily confined to reading for an arts degree. It embraced a study of Latin, Greek, Aristotle's logic, grammar, and metaphysics for which, as in Chaucer's time, he would require :—

> Twenty bookes, clothed in black and reed,
> Of Aristotil and of his philosophie.

Later he would be required to take part in disputations in the medical school, and acquire a knowledge of anatomy. The old Anatomy School was housed in a first-floor room on the south side of the Bodleian Quadrangle, but in 1683, during Dover's third year of residence, anatomy lectures were held in the newly opened Ashmolean Museum. Subjects for dissection were criminals executed on the gallows of Oxford or Abingdon, where the ardent students often had to face a riotous mob in order to secure the corpse. One human body was dissected during Lent term, and students were compelled to attend for four two-hourly lectures on the dissected part. During the autumn term three lectures on the human skeleton were given. Under a charter of Charles I the lecturer in anatomy was empowered to demand the body of any criminal executed within a twenty-mile radius of Oxford. The bodies were claimed immediately after the Lent assizes. It was then decreed that the corpse " be dissected by a skilful Chirurgeon in the Presence of his Proffessor, who is publickly to read thereon, and to shew and describe the Situation, Use, Nature and Office of all the Parts of the Body, at four distinct lectures, as prescrib'd in the Statutes made for this purpose. This lecturer is also every Michaelmas Term to read three distinct Lectures on a Skeleton, and to give an account of the Bones and their Office, Situation, etc."[1] Botany, then an important part of the medical course, was represented by the Physic Garden. It was, according to Ayliffe, as good as " any Place of Europe (if not the best) as also for the Service of all Medicinal Practitioners ".[2]

It was not a particularly distinguished period in Oxford medicine during Dover's residence. There was a lull in medical science following the astonishing achievements of the 'Invisible College' a few decades earlier. This brilliant collection of independent investigators had now forsaken Oxford for London, leaving only the official teachers who at that time were regrettably undistinguished. James Hyde was succeeded as Professor of Medicine by John Luffe, who was, according to Terræ Filius, a most lethal physician. He gives an account of a conversation between Drs. Luffe and Ludwell when they " met in a place they fill'd, viz. St. Thomas's Church-yard ".[3]

Many of the more progressive physicians completed their medical training in Continental universities, Leyden, Montpellier, and Padua being the ones most frequented. Their reason for going abroad was, according to the Reverend Andrew Clark, because " real students of medicine recognised that Oxford gave no opportunities for medical study and

---

[1] *Laudian Statutes*, Title IV, Section 1, cap. 15.

[2] J. AYLIFFE, *The Ancient and Present State of the University of Oxford*, 1714, Vol. II, 90.

[3] H. M. SINCLAIR and A. H. T. ROBB-SMITH, *Teaching of Anatomy in Oxford*, 1950, 16.

sought elsewhere the instruction which they could not obtain at home ".[1]

At the beginning of Thomas Dover's second year of residence a new Parliament was summoned to meet at Oxford. It was the last of three short-lived assemblies wherein the chief topic of disputation was a Bill for excluding James, Duke of York, from succession to the throne. Some years earlier Titus Oates had revealed a Popish conspiracy which Parliament condemned as " a damnable and hellish Plot ". This alleged conspiracy aroused strong anti-Catholic feeling throughout the country which led to their persecution. Shaftesbury and the Opposition then seized the opportunity of endeavouring to prevent the succession of James (who was known to have pronounced Roman Catholic sympathies) in favour of the Duke of Monmouth, an illegitimate son of Charles II. Indeed, it was maintained by his supporters that the Duke of Monmouth was legitimate, and that his parents' marriage certificate had been secreted in " a certain black box ".

Charles II expected that this issue would cause much rioting in Oxford, and desired that the younger students, and all who were not engaged in public duties, should leave the University early and remain away whilst Parliament was in session. This leave of absence was allowed to count as residence by royal decree. Thus Oxford became the centre of affairs, and the magnet of important personages. The first to arrive was George Villiers, Duke of Buckingham, who visited Oxford to lend support at the elections. Sir Christopher Wren, then Surveyor General, was in charge of arrangements for the King's reception ; and a few weeks later the Duke of Brunswick and Lunenberg (afterwards George I) visited Oxford, where he was created Doctor of Civil Law. Finally, on March 19th, 1681, amidst a tumultuous university reception, Charles II arrived in the city which had so loyally supported his father.

The King took up residence at Christ Church, and was followed a few days later by the Duke of Monmouth, who was

---

[1] ANDREW CLARKE, *The Register of the University of Oxford*, 1887, Vol. II, Pt. I, 123.

very quietly received. But the Oxford Parliament was only of short duration, as within ten days of his arrival, the King ordered its dissolution and returned to his capital. The royal visit served to stimulate jealousies between Town and Gown. The University Tory and City Whig were constantly quarrelling and brawling in the streets and taverns. On one such occasion the proctors carried off a townsman to the Castle, but the mob threatened the unfortunate Proctor who had to be rescued by the Vice-Chancellor.

Religious bigotry was also very pronounced. When elected a Freeman of the City of Oxford during the previous year Lord Lovelace had proposed a toast " to the confusion of all Popish Princes " : but after the King's visit Lady Lovelace was pulled out of her coach by gentlemen commoners, and called " an old protesting bitch ".[1] Religious differences became so strident as to degenerate into coarseness and brutality. Although religion was so frequently the main topic of conversation, there is ample evidence of moral degeneration. A Master of Arts of New Inn Hall was expelled " for biting off a piece of the nose " of a Bachelor of Arts from Brasenose College following a scuffle in the Parks. Neale's diary reveals many more instances of the general lack of discipline in the University, of which the following account is an example :—

At the end of this month drunken fighting took place in St. John's common room. There is a knot of four undergraduates known to be notorious atheists. They come drunk into the chapel and vomit in their hats or caps there. . . . There is no sin but they are guilty of. . . . The next College that wants a thorough reformation is New College, much given to drinking and gambling and vain brutish pleasure. They degenerate in learning.[2]

The social life of undergraduates was varied. Shooting with the long bow was in favour ; bowls was frequently played, and maintained its popularity throughout the century—both these exercises being recommended for gravel and the stone. Tilting, throwing, leaping, wrestling, running, and swimming were commoner pastimes, and bell-ringing, an

---

[1] C. M. NEALE, Bodleian MSS., 1660–1737, Top. Oxon. c.257, 244.
[2] Ibid., 237.

amusement of early origin, was still in vogue, though, according to Wordsworth, it was often attended with severe injuries such as broken bones. " Tuft-hunting ", the obsequious pursuit of scions of the nobility and other gentlemen commoners, who wore a gold tassel or tuft on their college caps, was not uncommon. Sir Charles Mallett[1] states that the Duke of Beaufort at the age of fifteen was evidently a considerable personage at University College, and respect for the boy's years did not prevent one of the fellows from drinking with him until two o'clock in the morning. Dover, though he prided himself on his independence, was not immune from this form of snobbery, at any rate in later life.

Thomas Dover graduated Bachelor of Arts on July 1st, 1684. In the following year national events again ruffled the surface of Oxford life. Charles II died, and James was proclaimed King at Oxford by Lord Abingdon, " the conduits running claret all the while ".[2] Two months after his coronation, Oxford's drums again beat out a call for volunteers. The Duke of Monmouth had landed near Lyme and was soon afterwards proclaimed king at Taunton. Members of the University were rapidly mobilized and known rebel sympathizers (chiefly amongst the townspeople) were imprisoned.

Muskets and pikes were sent from Windsor, and most of the colleges raised companies of scholar-soldiers, who began preparing the defences of city and university. The company at Christ Church was commanded by Captain the Lord Norreys, then aged fifteen. Thomas Dover might well have been a member of the Magdalen company. On July 1st, 1685, news reached Oxford that the rebels had been defeated and celebrations were begun. They ceased when the news proved false ; but six days later Monmouth was defeated at Sedgemoor and subsequently executed.

Then came the trial of conscience. In his ardour for Romanism, James II exerted arbitrary power by insisting on the election of Catholic Principals and Fellows. But in so

---

[1] Sir Charles Mallett, A History of the University of Oxford, 1924, Vol. III, 64.

[2] C. M. Neale, Bodleian MSS., 1660–1737, Top. Oxon. C.257, 261.

doing the King struck a fatal blow against the security of his throne. The Fellows of Magdalen were summoned to Whitehall for their failure to elect the King's Roman Catholic nominee as President, and later twenty-five of them were expelled. Mass was said regularly at Christ Church and University College, and the whole University was rapidly becoming a Jesuit seminary. The University of Oxford, which had been for so long the stronghold of Royalist principles, was now agitated by passions never known before. Indeed, so mutinous was the temper of the University that the newly organized regiment of Dragoon Guards was quartered there in order to keep the peace. The culmination came when James ordered the arrest of seven Anglican Bishops for refusing to read his declaration of freedom of conscience in their churches. The vested interests of Anglican orthodoxy could not tolerate a Catholic monarchy (made practically certain by the birth of an heir to James), and so the news of the landing of William of Orange on November 3, 1688, was welcomed in Oxford.

The prevalence of infectious diseases was briefly recorded by many contemporary writers. With the exception of the plague (which had created so much havoc fifty years earlier and was in Dover's time regarded as exceptional) yearly epidemics of typhoid, typhus, malaria, and small-pox were the accepted burden of the times. During each of the six years of Dover's Oxford residence the city was visited by several epidemic fevers. The most severe outbreaks occurred in the summer or autumn. In the autumn of 1681, for instance, Neale records that " a pestilential fever " raged in Oxford as a result of which " many are sick and some die ".[1] This outbreak may well have been due to benign tertian malaria which reached its peak in the autumn, as typhoid, plague, and small-pox were attended with a much higher mortality. The following year " from Spring until this time (Autumn) a malignant fever in Oxford "[2] possibly referred to intermittent fevers of spring, which during a hot dry summer led to further

---

[1] C. M. NEALE, Bodleian MSS., 1660–1737, Top. Oxon. C257, 230.
[2] *Ibid.*, 238.

2

infection, and usually reached a peak in the autumn. The spring intermittents described by Sydenham were made up of relapses from the preceding year, whilst his autumnal intermittents represented new malarial infections.

The severe small-pox epidemic of 1683 gave Dr. John Radcliffe an opportunity of practising the cooling method of treatment recently advocated by Dr. Sydenham. The " new method ", as it was called by the illustrious Locke, was disregarded by the majority of physicians, who were still content to trudge the ancient course. But evidently Dr. Radcliffe found Sydenham's recommendations highly successful, as in the following year he left Oxford, and within a remarkably short time was established as the most fashionable physician in London.

Such was the Oxford of Dover's day. In a city plagued by recurrent fevers, and against a background of political unrest, the University stirred uneasily under the newly awakened scientific stimulus. It was still a time of religious bigotry, with moral laxity and brutality well to the fore ; whilst of all the University faculties, that of medicine still slumbered on in spite of the earlier brilliant achievements.

It appears that academic considerations influenced Dover's change of university in 1686, as *Alumni Cantabrigienses* contains the following entry :—

Dover, Thomas—Adm. pens. at Caius, Nov. 4 1686 ; M.B. 1687. Son of John, of Barton-on-the-Heath, Warwks., Gent. Bapt. there May 6 1662, Matric. from Magdalen Hall, Oxford, Dec. 1 1680, " aged 16 " ; B.A. 1684.[1]

No doubt the medical reputation which Caius College then enjoyed influenced Dover to change universities just before qualification. At that time Dr. Robert Brady was Master of Caius College, where his activities were displayed in two widely different spheres. He had been appointed Professor of Physic in 1677 and was successively physician to Charles II and James II, but his only known professional communication is a letter to his friend Sydenham in whose works it is published. Brady makes inquiries about Peruvian bark, and

---

[1] *Alumni Cantabrigienses*, 1922, Vol. II, Pt. 1, 59.

suggests the advisability of less severe bleeding than was usually recommended at the time. However, he must have been held in high repute as a private physician in order to have been selected for royal service. Brady was often in attendance on the King, and the following is an extract from one of his accounts :—

Dr. Robert Brady, physician-in-ordinary to His Majesty . . . for his ryding charges and other expenses for himself, his men and horses in his attendance upon His Majesty at Windsor, for 144 days : at Winchester 30 days : at Newmarket 20 days : at the usuall rate of 25 shillings by the day.[1]

But it is as an historian that Brady is best known. In his capacity as Keeper of Records at the Tower, he enjoyed the advantage of easy access to original manuscripts from which his printed works prove that he was a careful and laborious scholar. Amongst his best known historical works is *A Complete History of England*, published in 1685. Brady was also Member of Parliament for Cambridge University, in which role he was a most zealous upholder of royal authority and prerogative, over Parliamentary and constitutional rights.

College life had completely recovered from the Civil War and was generally more settled than at Oxford. During Dover's brief residence at Cambridge the colleges were more luxurious. The surplice was made compulsory at chapel service ; fasting was reintroduced, and the custom of laymen giving addresses at the service was gradually discontinued.

Amongst Dover's contemporaries at Caius was Elias Duffy of " elixir " fame, who graduated at the same time. Another medical student at Caius was James Drake, who became a Fellow of the Royal Society, but is best known for his political writings on the Tory side. Several of his pamphlets brought him into trouble. He was prosecuted for his *History of the Last Parliament* (1702) and later for his *Memorial of the Church of England* (1704) which was burnt by the public hangman. Drake was convicted of libel for some of his passages in *Mercurius Politicus*. He also wrote plays and several anatomical works. Another Cambridge contemporary was Thomas

---

[1] JOHN VENN, *History of Gonville and Caius College*, 1901, 150.

Crow, who subsequently became a Fellow of the College of Physicians and many years later was elected Censor, at the time when Thomas Dover applied for admission as a licentiate.

After graduating Bachelor of Medicine in 1687, Thomas Dover went as a house pupil of Dr. Sydenham, the most distinguished physician of his generation.

CHAPTER III

SYDENHAM'S PUPIL

Our Physick Doctor next took his Degree,
In hopes the Title may enlarge the Fee,
The Ladies Doctor—let him feel your Pulse,
I'm sure he need desire no Business else.

ROGER LONG

THROUGHOUT Sydenham's lifetime, and until nearly a century after his death when his works had their full impact, clinical medicine drifted uneasily in the doldrums of humoral pathology. Physicians still tended to interpret pathological processes in terms of an imbalance between the ' four humours ', which in turn were said to correspond to the four ' temperaments '. They were formal scholars, heavily laden with the traditions of the schools : their diagnoses and clinical judgements, based on hypothetical classifications of disease, were but slightly related to the particular patients under their care.

The scientific awakening at the beginning of the seventeenth century had a profound effect on the basic sciences of anatomy and physiology, but only slightly influenced the actual practice of medicine. Indeed, some of these purely scientific ideas were fantastic when applied to clinical problems and pushed to extreme limits. However, they were destined to serve as stepping stones to greater wisdom.

One continental ' school ' of scientists likened the body to a machine, and sought to explain all the intricacies of health and disease as being purely mechanical or physical in nature. They were the exponents of the iatrophysical theory, which had been given a great impetus by the discoveries of Galileo, and the demonstrations of Sanctorius. But physiological processes could not, of course, be explained in these terms.

So another school, with many English disciples, preferred to view life as a series of chemical reactions. Disciples of the iatrochemical school (for such was it named) were wont to regard biological processes as akin to a series of test-tube reactions. A prominent advocate of this theory was Franciscus Sylvius (1614–72), Professor of Medicine at Leyden, whose most significant work was the study of salts derived from the union of acid and base. Largely as a result of his purely chemical research, the followers of Sylvius tended to express all forms of vital activity in terms of ' acid ', ' alkali ', and ' fermentation '.

This trend of research, though a great scientific advance, brought the added danger of detracting the physician's interest still further away from the *actual clinical study of diseases* by detailed observation. But the wisdom of Thomas Sydenham was such that without alining himself with any ' school ', he brought clinical medicine back again to the detailed study of the natural history of disease ; and thus largely contributed to the sober empiricism which is still a characteristic of clinical medicine. It was not his intention to promote systematic science, some aspects of which he certainly undervalued. It was rather to hold up to over-confident Science its perpetual counterpart and corrective in the shape of simple observation.

Dr. Singer[1] points out that Sydenham's views were in many ways a return to the Hippocratic conception of the " healing power of Nature ", which had been obscured during the twenty centuries that separated these two physicians. Sydenham's book *Methodus Curandi Febres* opens with a sentence that echoes the Hippocratic view :—" A disease, in my opinion, how prejudicial soever its causes may be to the body, is no more than a vigorous effort of Nature to throw off the morbific matter and thus recover the patient."[2]

Thomas Sydenham was descended from a wealthy Puritan family, and had interrupted his studies at Oxford in order to serve the Parliamentarians during the Civil War. On his return to Oxford his friends included Robert Boyle the

---

[1] CHARLES SINGER, *A Short History of Medicine*, 132.
[2] THOMAS SYDENHAM, *Methodus Curandi Febres*, 1666, Preface, 1.

chemist, and at a later date John Locke, physician and philosopher. After completing his studies Sydenham was elected to a fellowship at All Souls ; but shortly afterwards he was recalled to the army when Charles II landed in Scotland. During this second campaign, in which he was twice wounded, Sydenham served as a Captain of Horse. His medical knowledge was not unused during the war, as he " physicked " his men as well as leading them into action. When the rebellion ended, Sydenham returned to All Souls for a short time before continuing his studies at Montpellier. In 1661 he began to practise in Westminster, from where he commenced his life-long study of epidemic diseases.

Thomas Sydenham was manly and simple. His manner was more characteristic of a Captain of Horse than of a polished courtly physician ; for he was a man of action when most physicians were men of books. But when Thomas Dover became his pupil around 1687, Sydenham's work was virtually finished. He was a tired, ailing man near the end of his span. From early life he had suffered from gout, to which in later years was added the more painful condition of renal calculus, for which he prescribed himself a moderate diet with liberal fluids. His favourite drink was small beer, " to cool and dilute the hot and acrid juices lodged in the kidney ; out of which the stone is formed ".[1]

He lived in Pall Mall, next to the " Pestle and Mortar ", the shop of his apothecary Mr. Malthus ; and it was here that another pupil, Hans Sloane, also stayed about the same time as Thomas Dover. The two pupils were destined to meet many years later, when Sloane presided over both the College of Physicians and the Royal Society.

During his short apprenticeship Thomas Dover would be taught to apply his theoretical knowledge in the diagnosis and treatment of disease. At the present time such a procedure seems axiomatic, but the majority of seventeenth-century physicians remained repositories of theoretical doctrines all their lives. They had slight contact with their patients, who were usually treated through an intermediary—the apothecary.

---

[1] *Entire Works of Thomas Sydenham*, 1753, 3rd ed., 492. Ed. John Swann.

But Dover was fortunate in having a practical tutor who was interested in studying the causation of disease, as well as in treating the individual patients under his care. The routine duties of Sydenham's apprentice would therefore quite frequently bring him to the patient's bedside. There he would be taught the art of simple observation as an essential preliminary to accurate diagnosis. He would also be taught to prescribe medicine, and would accompany his master at discussions with apothecaries and surgeons.

Sydenham's views on the practice of medicine are expressed in his many published works, which can also be assumed to reflect the gist of his verbal teaching.

Firstly, he expected his apprentices to maintain the high moral and ethical standards exemplified in his own practice. Sydenham's *religio medici* is clearly expressed in the preface to his book on fevers :—

> Whoever applies himself to medicine ought seriously to weigh the following considerations. First, that he will one day have to render an account to the Supreme Judge of the lives of sick persons admitted to his care. Next, whatever skill or knowledge he may, by Divine favour, become possessed of, should be devoted above all things to the glory of God and the welfare of the human race. Moreover, let him remember that it is not any base or despicable creature of which he has undertaken the care. For the only begotten Son of God, by becoming man, recognised the value of the human race, and ennobled by His own dignity the nature He assumed. Finally, the physician should bear in mind that he himself is not exempt from the common lot, but subject to the same laws of mortality and disease as others ; and he will care for the sick with more diligence and tenderness if he remembers that he himself is their fellow-sufferer.[1]

Another important art which Sydenham certainly taught his pupils was that of detailed observation at the bedside. Sydenham himself always took notes of the signs, symptoms, course, and seasonal incidence of the diseases he treated ; and it is probable that he expected his pupils to do likewise. He was essentially a practical physician, with plenty of sound common sense, an eye for detail, and a distaste for the then too fashionable literary approach to medicine. He put aside the theories, facts, and fictions collected out of books, which

---

[1] THOMAS SYDENHAM, *Methodus Curandi Febres*, 1666, Preface, 1.

he says, "have as much to do with treating sick men as the
painting of pictures has to do with the sailing of ships".[1]

In his general description of diseases, Sydenham paid
particular attention to epidemic fevers, which in those days
comprised more than two-thirds of medical practice. He
divided fevers into three main divisions: continued fevers,
intermittent fevers, and small-pox. His observations on these
various groups were gathered from the study of epidemics
between 1661 and 1676. During these fifteen years he
witnessed five different periods, each of which was characterized by what he terms an *epidemic* constitution, or disposition
of the atmosphere, which in turn contributed to an outbreak
of the corresponding fever: "If one were to examine all the
branches of physic nothing would appear so surprising as the
different and perfectly dissimilar face of epidemic diseases;
which do not so much relate to, and depend upon the
various seasons of the same year, as upon the different
constitutions of different years."[2]

During the first period he studied (1661–4) intermittent
fevers predominated, accompanied by a peculiar species of
continued fever. Pestilential fevers raged during the second
period (1665–6); and the third period was conspicuous for
the variolous constitution when small-pox was rampant.
Sydenham also observed the seasonal incidence of epidemics,
which were influenced by climatic factors: "Again, it must
be observed, that all epidemics are of two sorts, viz. vernal
and autumnal, and tho' they may possibly arise at a distant
time of the year, yet they must be refer'd either to spring or
autumn, according as they approach thereto respectively.
For sometimes the temperature of the air conspires so
much with an epidemic disease, as to produce it before its
time."[3]

Sydenham's general conception of fevers, owing their
changing characteristics, partly to the particular constitution
of the year, and partly to the prevailing epidemic, was further
complicated by his prognostications. If, for example, a

---

[1] F. J. PAYNE, *Thomas Sydenham*, 1900, 137.
[2] *Entire Works of Thomas Sydenham*, 1753, 4. Ed. John Swann.
[3] *Ibid.*, 6.

certain fever was raging, then the concomitant disease (such as measles or dysentery) could be predicted *without* even seeing a case.

His classification of continued fevers seems somewhat vague to us, as there was then no notion of specific organisms giving rise to particular fevers. Nevertheless it was a good practical approach. It was his belief that a natural period of fourteen days for "fermentation" to take place was common to this group of fevers. This observation may well have been based on his knowledge of typhus (the most characteristic fever in this group) which has been called the 'fourteen days fever', as it usually terminates within that time. One of Sydenham's most sage observations was that a continued fever may usher in an intermittent fever, particularly during the autumn. He explains that intermittent fevers "do not perfectly put on their shapes . . . for they imitate continued fever so well that it is hard to distinguish them. But the violence of the constitution being a little quelled, and its strength checked, having thrown off the mask they then openly are seen to be intermittents, either tertian or quartans, as indeed they really were at first."[1]

Sydenham's powers of observation are most evident when treating intermittent fevers or the agues. He maintained that English malaria comprised two distinct varieties of the disease—the intermittents of spring, and those of autumn. Also he noticed that the "autumn intermittent" had been gaining ground during the hot dry summers, particularly during the one of 1661. Sydenham's "spring intermittents", which were self-limiting infections not requiring Peruvian bark for their suppression, are now known to be relapses from the previous year. Whilst his "autumnal intermittents", requiring treatment, represented new malarial infections.[2]

It is also quite certain that Sydenham devoted much of his teaching to the study of small-pox. The fact that he thought that this disease was a natural process which almost everyone had to go through at least once in his lifetime demonstrates

---

[1] *Entire Works of Thomas Sydenham*, 1753, 55. Ed. John Swann.
[2] W. P. MacArthur, "Malaria in England," *Brit. med. Bull.*, 1951, **8**, 76.

its universality in his day. Thomas Dover contracted small-pox whilst Sydenham's house pupil, and nearly half a century later briefly describes his master's treatment :—

"Whilst I lived with Dr. Sydenham," he writes, "I had myself the small-pox and fell ill on the twelfth day. In the beginning I lost 22 ounces of blood. He gave me a vomit, but I find by experience purging much better. I went abroad by his direction, till I was blind, and then took to my bed. I had no fire allowed in my room, my windows were constantly open, my bedclothes were ordered to be laid no higher than my waist. He made me take twelve bottles of small beer acidulated with spirits of vitriol every twenty-four hours. I had of this Anomalous kind to a very great degree, yet never lost my senses one moment. This method will serve very well in the confluent sort; this you may follow in the distinct smallpox but in a more remiss degree."[1]

This is a brief description of Sydenham's ' cooling method ' which was then a novel form of treatment. This same method was also followed by Dover in the treatment of all fevers, and undoubtedly accounted for much of his later success. Contemporary accounts show that at this time, and even until many years after Sydenham's death, small-pox patients were subjected to a so-called "hot" regimen. They were put to bed, kept well covered, and given stimulating cordials. "By such means", says Sydenham, "greater slaughters are committed, and more havocke made of man-kinde every yeare than hath bin made in any age by the sword of the fiercest and most bloody Tyrant that the world ever produced."[2]

At the onset of the disease, Sydenham confined the patient indoors, and ordered a light diet. Then, instead of following the common practice, he "immediately forbid a hotte regimen, and the use of all kinds of cordials, whereby some injudiciously endeavour to force out the smallpox before the fourth day, which is the natural and proper time for the eruption; for I am very sure that the slower the pustules come out, the more general the separation of the variolous matter will be, the better they will ripen, and the less danger there will be of them striking in : whereas if they be driven

[1] THOMAS DOVER, The Ancient Physician's Legacy, 1742, 6th ed., 119.

[2] MS. entitled "Medical Observations by Thomas Sydenham, London, Martii 26 1669." Royal College of Physicians of London.

out too soon, the matter, being yet crude and indigested, is precipitated and deceives our expectation, like over early fruit."[1]

This view was quite revolutionary, as hitherto treatment had been directed at driving out all the manifestations of disease (such as pustules) by the most expeditious means. Hence physicians were in the habit of keeping their patients warm, and giving them stimulating drinks. As in Dover's treatment, the patient was usually kept out of bed until the eruption was due to appear. " But on the fourth day I order the patient to be put to bed, at which time, if the eruption does not come kindly forward, it is proper to give some gentle cardiac (he mentions liquid laudanum) at least once to drive out the pustules."[2]   Here again Sydenham echoes the Hippocratic view of healing in harmony with Nature.

But Sydenham was far from being dogmatic in the manner of treatment, which he varied according to the particular epidemic, the type of small-pox, the age of the patient, and the presence of any complicating symptoms, such as diarrhœa. In the main, however, he allowed liberal fluids in the form of small beer, only a few bedclothes, and adequate bleeding, particularly in the case of young men, when an emetic was also given. As a general rule the younger and stronger the patient, the longer was he kept out of bed, in order not " to raise a sweat " ; as Sydenham believed that " bloody urine, purple spots, and other mortal symptoms "[3] arose from confining young people to bed too early.

Also regarded as specific fevers, and not as febrile diseases arising from local conditions, were erysipelas, rheumatism, and quinsy : iliac passion (appendicitis) was also included with the general fevers, for the treatment of which Sydenham recommended the application of a live puppy to the patient's abdomen.

As well as a thorough grounding in the knowledge of epidemic fevers, Dover would be taught all that was then known about many other conditions. His master was the

[1] *Entire Works of Thomas Sydenham*, 1753, 198.   Ed. John Swann.
[2] *Ibid.*, 120.
[3] *Ibid.*

first to describe hysteria, which he regarded as an ataxia of the
" animal spirits ", which, when referred to other parts of
the body, created " the proper symptoms of the part ".[1]
A complete understanding of this affliction is still wanting.
Yet providing ' nervous energy ' is substituted for ' animal
spirits ', then Sydenham's description and his explanation of
hysteria still conform with the modern conception of a
psychosomatic disease. His knowledge of the precipitating
factors, together with his vivid description of an actual attack,
are such that they have never been surpassed, and remain to
this day absolutely classical.

Sydenham's description of dropsy was of less value, as he
tended to ignore the mechanical causes, and instead vaguely
referred to the condition as a " watery state of the blood ".[2]
His last book was published in 1686, just before Dover joined
him, and contains the first description of St. Vitus's dance,
or the type of chorea which is still known by his name.

Also in the matter of treatment, Thomas Dover had a
teacher who was conversant with each new therapeutic
measure. Though not the first to use Peruvian bark in
England, Sydenham's writings greatly helped to popularize
its use. There was some prejudice against the drug in
England as it was associated with the Jesuits, and because
many bogus preparations not containing quinine were
commonly sold. He was also one of the first physicians to
recommend iron in the treatment of chlorosis, although in
this respect his pupil Dover, when writing later of the ' green
sickness ', suggested that it was due to the common practice
of tight lacing amongst young girls. " Since mothers have
been so foolishly desirous for nice shapes for their children,
and in tender years have laced them so very straight, they
have not only brought on this distemper more early, but
caused great crookedness and deformity of the body."[3]

But Dover's advice and treatment were hardly suitable
for the unemancipated state of women in seventeenth-century
England.

---

[1] *Entire Works of Thomas Sydenham*, 1753, 415. Ed. John Swann.
[2] *Ibid.*, 516.
[3] THOMAS DOVER, *The Ancient Physician's Legacy*, 1742, 6th ed., 71.

Let mankind take a view of the barbarous countries as I have done and contemplate those people where God and Nature have only been ; observe in what order and delicacy their muscles are placed, how strong their bodies, how taper their limbs. There are no full shoulders nor gummy thighs nor legs, nor any deformity. All parts are conspicuous, since the natives have no more clothing than what our first parents had during the short time of their innocence. In some places they have not so much as a fig leaf to conceal the distinctions of either sex.[1]

However, this same view has persisted until the present century and the disappearance of chlorosis is still regarded by some physicians as being due to a change in feminine fashions.

Sydenham stressed the value of opium, more than any other drug, which he introduced in liquid form as a ' tincture of laudanum ' ; a preparation which soon displaced the solid pills then in common use. " Without opium, without hypnotics and the medicines made from these, medicine would be helpless and crippled ", was one of Sydenham's famous dicta.[2] Thomas Dover perpetuated his master's teaching by adding opium to the composition of the powder which still bears his name.

Thomas Dover's teacher was also an exponent of expectant treatment, at a time when the writing of extended prescriptions with many ingredients for each symptom was much in vogue. Helping the patient's natural resistance to overcome infection, and intervening only should complications arise, was an important part of Sydenham's method of practice. As he so justly writes, " The pomp and dignity of the art of medicine lie not so much in the skillful concoction of drugs as in the cure of the disease."[3]

But as was only to be expected, his views were not invariably accurate. He refused to allow that mercury was a specific in the treatment of syphilis. " Whoever (with respect to the venereal disease) asserts that mercury and sarsaparilla are two alexipharmics for the virus thereof should produce some examples."[4] Yet his favourite method of administration was in the form of an unction of hog's lard and mercury which

---

[1] THOMAS DOVER, *The Ancient Physician's Legacy*, 1742, 6th ed., 114.
[2] *Entire Works of Thomas Sydenham*, 1753, 448. Ed. John Swann.
[3] *Ibid.*, 1.
[4] *Ibid.*, 83.

was used to produce a salivation of approximately four pints in twenty-four hours. In this respect Dover's later treatment was drastically different from that of his old teacher.

However, there can be no doubt that Sydenham's teaching had a profound effect on Thomas Dover's subsequent practice. Nearly fifty years later, when Dover published his popular medical book, he still mentions his old teacher's name in affectionate terms : a rare compliment from one who, by then, had become somewhat irate and overbearing. When treating of consumption, Dover writes : " The good Doctor Sydenham wonderfully commends Riding in this distemper . . . But with deference to my old friend's judgment I have known frequent bleeding in small quantities to do more good than Riding."[1]

Again, when advocating bleeding in the treatment of small-pox Dover adds, " The good Dr. Sydenham goes no further than ' Mithatur sanguis quovis die ante tertium inclusive ', which is but the second day after their appearance."[2]

But the most surprising similarity of treatment between Sydenham and his pupil is that of massive bleeding in the treatment of plague. Sydenham mentions that during the Civil War he heard of a surgeon who (having learnt the treatment abroad) treated the defenders of Dunster Castle in Somerset for the plague. The men were bled at the onset of the disease before the buboes were apparent : the surgeon then " took away so large a quantity of blood . . . that they were ready to faint and drop down ; for he bled them all standing, and in the open air, and had no vessels to measure the blood, which falling on the ground, the quantity of each person lost could not of course be known. The operation being over, he ordered them to lie in their tents and tho' he gave no kind of remedy after bleeding, yet of the numbers that were thus treated not a single person died ; which is surprising."[3]

Sydenham goes on to say that he also had found this method useful in many instances, though on the whole he preferred to

---

[1] THOMAS DOVER, *The Ancient Physician's Legacy*, 1742, 6th ed., 31.
[2] *Ibid.*, 114.
[3] *Entire Works of Thomas Sydenham*, 1753, 87. Ed. John Swann.

"dissipate the pestileutial ferment by sweat" rather than bleeding.[1]

As a prelude to his account of the plague, Dover refers again to his late teacher : " Read the man whose reason was much superior to mine ", he says, " the honest and good Dr. Sydenham, and see if the rule (treating fevers by contaries) was not his guide."[2]   Then, in a flamboyant manner, Dover recounts the following tale from his travels which bears a remarkable similarity to the episode mentioned by Sydenham.

When I took by storm the twin cities of Guiaquil, under the line in the South Seas, it happened that not long before the plague had raged amongst them.   For our better security, therefore, and for keeping our people together we lay in their churches, and likewise brought thither the plunder of the cities.   We were very much annoyed with the smell of dead bodies. The bodies could hardly be said to be buried for the Spaniards abroad used no coffins, but throw several dead bodies upon one another with only a drawboard over them.   So that 'tis no wonder that we received the infection.   In a few days after we got on board, one of the surgeons came to acquaint me that several of my men were taken after a violent manner with such languor of spirits that they were not able to move.   I immediately went amongst them and to my surprise soon discerned what was the matter. In less than forty-eight hours we had in our several ships, one hundred and eighty men in this miserable condition.   I ordered the surgeons to bleed them in both arms and to go round to them all, with command to leave them bleeding till they were blooded, and then come and tie them up in their turns.   Thus they lay bleeding and fainting till so long as I could not conceive they could lose less than a hundred ounces each man.   We had on board oil and spirit of vitriol sufficient ; which I caused to be mixed with water to the acidity of a lemon, and made them drink very freely of it, so that notwithstanding we had one hundred and eighty odd down in this most fatal distemper, yet we lost no more than seven or eight and even these owed their deaths to the strong liquors which their mess-mates procured for them.[3]

Dover's contemporaries certainly thought that much of his treatment was modelled on Sydenham's methods.   His most searching critic, Daniel Turner, accused Dover of ' borrowing ' his description of hypochondrial and hysterical diseases from Sydenham's account ; of ' stealing ' his quinsy gargle from Sydenham ; and again, when discussing small-pox Turner

---

[1] *Entire Works of Thomas Sydenham*, 1753, 87.   Ed. John Swann.

[2] THOMAS DOVER, *The Ancient Physician's Legacy*, 1742, 6th ed., 103.

[3] *Ibid.*, 100.

writes, " No man has given a more graphical Description of
them than the most industrious Sydenham, from whom this
gentleman has taken every Thing that is worthy of any
regard."[1]

In later life Thomas Dover developed a strong spirit of
independence in medical matters, which was also one of
Sydenham's characteristics. Routine and precedent had little
weight with Sydenham ; and there was probably a grain of
truth in what was said of him seriously by Blackmore,
scoffingly by Gideon Harvey, that he made it his principle to
go contrary to the practice of other physicians.

Though he had friends amongst the Fellows of the College
of Physicians, Sydenham was never elected to their numbers.
Dover's subsequent attacks on the college may have been
partly influenced (as being only a Bachelor of Medicine he
could not qualify for election himself) by memories of his
early days with Sydenham, whose sad omission first aroused
his antagonism against that august body.

Thus, at the house of Sydenham, ended Thomas Dover's
formal medical training. Even by modern standards he had
followed a lengthy course : six years at Oxford, one at
Cambridge, and a short apprenticeship with the most outstanding physician of his generation. Compared with
Sydenham's great achievements, Dover has left only a meagre
legacy in the form of a popular medical book wherein the
descriptions of disease are necessarily scanty. Though
obviously lacking his great teacher's ability and painstaking
powers of observation, nevertheless Dover was, like
Sydenham, a forthright, independent, and practical physician
who faithfully continued to follow his teacher's main
precepts throughout his life. It can therefore safely be
assumed that when Thomas Dover began his own practice
he was as well equipped (in the manner of training) as any
other physician of his time.

---

[1] DANIEL TURNER, *The Ancient Physician's Legacy Impartially Survey'd*,
1733, 41, 80, 103.

3

CHAPTER IV

MEDICAL PRACTICE IN DOVER'S TIME

There was also a Doctour of Physik,
In al this world ne was ther non him lyk
To speke of physik and of surgerye ;
For he was groundud in astronomye.
He kepte his pacient wondurly wel
In hours by his magik naturel.

CHAUCER

AFTER completing his short apprenticeship with Dr. Sydenham, Dover returned to Barton-on-the-Heath. Only his father and mother were now living there, as all his sisters had married early, and his brother John held the living of Drayton near Banbury. John Dover senior was now a substantial gentleman farmer, as in addition to his one hundred and fifty acres of farmland at Barton, he had also purchased other lands at Netterswell in Gloucestershire and at Stow-on-the-Wold. Therefore there was plenty of work for Thomas Dover ; helping his father with the farming, and establishing himself in a country practice which would necessitate many hours in the saddle. Captain Dover's failing health together with the need for active supervision of the farms, rather than the attraction of a country practice, probably influenced Thomas Dover's return to Barton.

The standard of education amongst country doctors was deplorably low. Even as late as 1816, the law did not require a country practitioner to follow any systematic training other than serving an apprenticeship with an empiric whose only information was the rudest elements of a druggist's art. Hence the arrival of a university graduate, and a physician to boot, would be a welcome addition to the meagre medical resources of the Cotswold villages.

Thomas Dover had married (probably in 1687), but his wife's identity is still unsolved. Her christian name (according to the Barton register) was Joanna, and she bore him twin daughters, Elizabeth and Magdalen, who were baptized at Barton on April 27th, 1688 ; but the same register records their burials only a few weeks later—Elizabeth on May 12th and Magdalen three days later. A third daughter, Sibilla, was baptized at Barton on December 8th, 1693. She subsequently married John Hunt, and left many descendants. Elizabeth Dover, the younger surviving daughter, who was born after the family had moved to Bristol, married John Opie, but died childless. Very little is known about Thomas Dover's family life, but judging from his writing he had an eye to feminine beauty. When over seventy, his wife having died six years previously, he displays a dash of gallantry when urging women to be inoculated against small-pox. " Yet what is very surprising ", he says, " it meets with little encouragement from the ladies. Is beauty that arrives to such perfection in an English climate of so little importance that it is beneath our care ? What miserable havock, what terrible changes has this one distemper produced in the most lovely and amiable part of creation ? The ladies may possibly smile to hear a man of seventy use such warm expressions, but I will venture to say with Mr. Dryden that,

' Old as I am, for ladies' love unfit
The power of beauty I remember yet '."[1]

Dr. Dover began his life as a physician at a time of great professional uneasiness, complicated by rampant quackery, and much jealousy amongst medical men. In an age when orthodox medicine so often failed to cure or alleviate many common diseases, suffering humanity usually fell back on the quack and his nostrums. Many irregular practitioners attained great wealth and fame by pandering to superstition and the inherent human capacity for self delusion.

Such a one was John Archer, a writer of disreputable books, and vendor of secret remedies for venereal disease, who styled himself " Chymical Physician to His Majesty ". Sir William

---

[1] THOMAS DOVER, *The Ancient Physician's Legacy*, 1742, 6th ed., 95.

Read, originally a teacher, later became " sworn oculist" to
Queen Anne, by whom he was knighted.   At a somewhat
later date there was Mrs. Mapp, or " Crazy Sally " as she was
known, who practised as a bone setter at Epsom and drove
once or twice a week to the Grecian Coffee House in a four-
wheeled chariot with gorgeously attired outriders.   Joshua
or " Spot " Ward was another adventurer, who attained great
wealth and eminence.   He was well aware of the power of
advertisement, and made it known that he would cure patients
pronounced incurable at several hospitals.   Sir D'Arcy Power
says that he fulfilled his promise " by the simple device of
hiring patients at two and sixpence a week and instructing
them in the symptoms of the disease they were to simulate.
A better class came in coaches and sat in his consulting room
at five shillings a day, Ward paying the coach hire."[1]

Another set of irregular practitioners were the astrologers,
who abounded in England during the seventeenth century.
Not content with drawing horoscopes and ordinary fortune-
telling, men like Culpeper and Lilly trespassed on the
province of the physician and practised physic by the light of
the stars.

There were others who practised outright chicanery.
These were the hordes of base empirics, herbalists, water-
casters and the like, who had no pretensions to chemistry or
astrology, but with abundant effrontery offered their remedies
for every complaint.   Mountebanks from country fairs
blowing their trumpets in the streets ; hawkers of amulets,
charms, nostrums ; charlatans and impostors of every name
and colour, plied their wares with little hindrance on the part
of the law.   Daniel Defoe, when deploring the practice of
newspapers (including his own) of accepting advertisements
for quack remedies, writes : " The Appearance of a Quack in
any part of the Country is a more certain Destruction to the
Men than a North West Wind to the Blossoms of the Spring ;
and I could predict plenty of Funerals from the former with
more Assurance than I could scarcity of Fruit from the

---

[1] Sir D'Arcy Power, *Johnson's England*, 1933, Vol. II, 275.   Ed. A. S.
Tuberville.

Latter."[1]   Matthews in his *Humours of a Country Fair* also ridicules the quack and his specific—" Sir, By the bursting of a powder mill, I was blown into ten thousand anatomies. The first bottle of your incomparable collected all the parts together—the second restored life and animation—before a third bottle was finished, I was in my usual state of health."[2]

Though laws were made against them, professional bodies seemed powerless to stop irregular practice. The only instance of intervention by the College of Physicians occurred late in the eighteenth century.   On this occasion a certain Dr. Brodum was summoned to attend a meeting of the college Censors in order to explain his authority for practising as a physician.   As the doctor was only acquainted with Hebrew and English, the President consented to address him in the latter tongue, whereupon Dr. Brodum stated that his authority for practising medicine was his diploma from the Marischal College, Aberdeen. " I suppose," observed a Censor, " a purchased diploma." " I don't know," replied the doctor, " what you mean by a purchased diploma ; I suppose all physicians who possess a diploma, paid for it. I should not have had a diploma had I not been considered worthy of it ; and as to my nervous cordial Dr. Warner, and other learned members of your college, have done me the honour to take it, and recommend it." To the question, " How long did you reside at Aberdeen? " the doctor replied, " I have never been there ",[3] and added that his certificate, which bore the signature of one of the leading members of the College of Physicians, had been obtained in London.

Quack doctors were particularly numerous in country districts, where they vended their wares unhindered by the law. Armed with a few gaily coloured medicines and a glib tongue, they deemed themselves qualified to cure all the ailments to which the children of Adam are subject. Daniel Defoe, who always had a finger on the national pulse, frequently denounced them in his newspapers. In another article he describes the arrival of the ' doctor ' in a splendid

---

[1] DANIEL DEFOE, *The Weekly Journal and Saturday's Post*, Oct. 31st, 1719.

[2] F. B. WINSLOW, *Physic and Physicians*, 1842, I, 343.

[3] *Ibid.*, 1842, I, 340.

coach attended by footmen who herald his approach to the
village with a fanfare of trumpets.   When a sufficiently large
crowd has gathered the ' doctor ' delivers a pretentious though
unintelligible speech, and then commences to sell his
medicines—the efficacy of which Defoe condemns with grim
humour.   " His bolus too is very good in its kind ; I have
made Experiments with it on several Animals and find that it
poisons to a Miracle.   A moderate Dose of it has perfectly
silenced a howling Dog that used to disturb my morning
Slumbers ; and a like quantity of it has quieted several other
Snarling Curs in my neighbourhood.   And then if you be
troubled with Rats, Mr. Mist, there's the Doctor's Electuary
is an infallible Remedy as I myself have experienced."[1]

Besides having to sustain competition from various kinds
of spurious doctors, the physicians' traditional practice was
also the poaching ground of surgeons and apothecaries.
Surgeons were not allowed to prescribe for internal maladies ;
nevertheless they often did so, particularly in country districts.

There was a small guild of pure surgeons which had grown
up during the Hundred Years War, but the majority were
barber-surgeons, who had served an apprenticeship, and were
usually freemen of the city in which they practised.   Their
insignia was a staff, porringer, and red garter.

When being bled, the patient would grasp the staff around
which was a tape used to bandage his arm ; and when not in
use, the pole was hung outside as a sign of the trade followed
within.   Until 1729 the poles of barber-surgeons were painted
red and white, in order to distinguish them from those of
mere barbers, whose colours were white and blue.   But some
barber-surgeons practised both arts, as did Henry Haines of
Bristol, who advertised his charges as twopence for a shave,
a penny-halfpenny for a haircut, and sixpence for bleeding :
after losing the requisite amount of blood, the customer was
given two quarts of free ale, but only one pint of ale was
given following a haircut.

The surgeons in the Bristol area were a well regulated body
throughout the seventeenth century ; no surgeon was allowed

---

[1] DANIEL DEFOE, *The Weekly Journal and Saturday's Post*, Dec. 5th, 1719.

to practise until he was considered sufficiently skilled in his art, and had been elected a freeman of the city. Surgeons were forbidden to " cure a wound or grief which is in danger to lose life or limb before he acquaints two or three of the chiefest and most skilful therewith, who may view the same cure before he take it in hand".[1]

Another dubious portal of entry to the medical profession arose from the licensing power vested in the Bishops during the reign of Henry VIII. Many episcopal licences were granted in the Bristol diocesis, and in 1670 the Bishop of Bristol tried to force even the barber-surgeons as well as irregular practitioners to take out these licences. An occasional licence was granted to an apothecary, and even as late as 1745 an episcopal licence was granted to an irregular practitioner in recognition of his long experience, and his treatise on diabetes.

Whilst Thomas Dover was still a country practitioner a great controversy was raging between physicians and apothecaries. The mutual obligation of the two practitioners was mentioned by Chaucer when describing his " Doctor of Physike " :—

> Full reddy hadde he his apothecaries
> To read him drugges and his letuaries
> For eche of him made other for to Winne
> Their friendship was not newe to beginne.[2]

Apothecaries were supposed to make up the physicians' prescriptions. They were originally tradesmen—grocers—and were not required to have any knowledge of medical science, nor were they to presume to administer drugs on their own judgement and responsibility. In Elizabeth I's reign William Bulleyn gives a list of regulations for apothecaries' guidance, and in rule nineteen their subordinate station is evident : " That he do remember his office is only to be ye physician's cooke."[3] But during the seventeenth century apothecaries began to prescribe medicines on their own

---

[1] George Parker, Bristol Med.-Chir. J., 1911, 29, 6.

[2] Poetical Works of Geoffrey Chaucer, Vol. 11, 14. Ed. Richard Morin.

[3] William Bulleyn, Bulwarke of Defence against all Sicknesse, Soarenesse and Wounds, etc., 1579, 51.

account without seeking the advice of a physician. The doctors of that day knew so little that the apothecaries found it easy to know as much. A knowledge of the herbals, an acquaintance with the ingredients and doses of a hundred empirical compounds, a system of maltreating eruptive fevers, gout, and consumption was all the practical knowledge they required. If they were threatened with censure or other punishment by a regular physician, they retorted by discontinuing to call him to consultations. Jealousies soon sprang up. Starving graduates were embittered by having to trudge the pavements of London and see the mean medicine-mixers dashing by in their carriages. Gideon Harvey, a contemporary physician, reckons the apothecaries had fifty to one hundred patients to the physician's one. " Hence ", he says, " five-sixths of the physicians go with their hands in their pockets all day, the greatest part of business passing only through few men's hands ; whereas there is scarce any little apothecary, but one time or another in the day there is life perceived in his mortar. Now this scarceness of business being by Physicians imputed to too great a share one hath before another makes them growl and snarl at one another, like so many barking animals at a bone in the water they can't come at."[1]

For many years the treatment of the sick poor had been largely the province of the apothecary, or the unlicensed practitioner. It was by this means that they first gained sufficient experience of diagnosis and treatment to begin prescribing on their own account to all and sundry. In order to remedy this practice, which threatened the livelihood of its members, the College of Physicians in 1687 voted that all members of the college, whether Fellows, Candidates, or Licentiates, should " give their advice gratis to all their neighbouring poor, when desired, within the City of London, or seven miles round ". But the poor folk, having seen a physician, carried their prescriptions to the apothecaries, only to learn that the trade charge for dispensing them was beyond their means. Whereupon the College of Physicians

---

[1] GIDEON HARVEY, *The Conclave of Physicians*, 1683, 48.

resolved to set up its own dispensary, where medicines could be purchased by the poor at cost price. Their suggestion was unanimously condemned by the apothecaries as a physicians' plot designed to steal their livelihood, rather than to help the poor. There was also dissension within the College, as many leading physicians did not wish to offend the apothecaries, on whom they depended for a large part of their income.

As a result the profession was split into dispensarians and anti-dispensarians. The apothecaries combined together and agreed not to recommend the dispensarians. Amongst these was Dover's fellow pupil, Hans Sloane, and Sir Samuel Garth, whose poem *The Dispensary* (in which he describes the old College of Physicians) did much to further their cause :—

> There stands a Dome, majestical to the Sight ;
> And sumptuous arches bear its oval Height,
> A golden globe plac'd high with artful skill
> Seems, to the distant sight, a Gilded Pill.[1]

Nine years after the project was first suggested a dispensary was built in Warwick Lane. Although we have no direct knowledge of Dover's attitude, and possible actions in this controversy, it may be inferred from his writing that he favoured the views of the dispensarians. He condemns the unethical conduct of the apothecaries in the following passage :—

The apothecaries, generally speaking, have it in their power to recommend the physician which is the wrongest step the patient can possibly take. The physician, to gratify the apothecary, thinks himself obliged to order ten times more physick than the patient really wants, by which means he often ruins his constitution and too often his life ; otherwise how is it possible an apothecary's bill in a fever should amount to forty, fifty or more pounds? I never affronted any apothecary unless ordering too little physick ; and curing a patient too soon, is in their way of thinking an unpardonable crime. I must confess, I could never bring an apothecary's bill to three pounds in a fever ; whereas I have known some of them in this disease to amount to forty, fifty or sixty pounds. If they can't cure with less charges, I can't forbear saying that I have the same opinion of their integrity as I have of their understanding.[2]

---

[1] SIR SAMUEL GARTH, *The Dispensary*, 1699, Canto 1, 1.
[2] THOMAS DOVER, *The Ancient Physician's Legacy*, 1742, 6th ed., 140.

Dover's strictures on the apothecaries, particularly his condemnation of the mercenary spirit amongst them, seem well justified, as many of them became exceedingly wealthy on the sufferings of the poor. Dover also accuses them of exceeding their duties, and assuming a physician's role; others were constantly asking the physician to vary his prescriptions (even though there were no medical grounds for such a procedure) in order to increase their gains. He writes :—

When I have attended some of my patients, they have very often given it as a reason for not seeing me that I do not prescribe every time I visit them and have likewise told me that they learned this doctrine from the Apothecary. "That 'tis your writing, physician only, that has a title to a fee." I must own at first sight, this carries a very good face with it, and must naturally create in patients a great opinion of the Apothecary, who seems in this respect to act merely out of regard to their welfare, and not out of any view to the Doctor's interest or his own. But to me it appears very plainly a deceit, however plausible to others ; and to make it clear to you, only consider, that if the physician writes it must be ten or twelve shillings at least to the Apothecaries' way ; and for my part I don't look upon this to be at all better than picking one man's pocket to put money into another's. Now I appeal to each unprejudiced reader whether, if a physician must be compelled to vary his prescriptions when there is no occasion for it, he is not consequently left under the greatest uncertainty, and incapable of judging what may or may not be of benefit to his patient? So that if such a practice does not prove fatal to the patient, he runs at least a very great hazard of his life.[1]

The protracted dissensions between physicians and apothecaries provided the poets and wits with a subject for discourse. Pope was a cordial supporter of the dispensarian physicians. In his *Essay on Criticism* he accused the critics of acquiring their slender knowledge of poetry from the poets they assailed ; and compared them with the apothecaries whose medical information was also pilfered from the prescriptions they were required to dispense.

> Then Criticism the Muse's handmaid proved,
> To dress her charms, and make her more beloved :
> But following wits from that intention strayed,
> Who could not win the mistress, wooed the maid ;

---

[1] THOMAS DOVER, *The Ancient Physician's Legacy*, 1742, 6th ed., 141.

> Against the poets their own arms they turned,
> Sure to hate most the men from whom they learned.
> So modern 'Pothecaries taught the art
> By Doctor's bills to play the Doctor's part,
> Bold in the practice of mistaken rules,
> Prescribe, apply, and call their masters fools.[1]

The dispensary controversy was waged with great vigour; and the literature of that squabble (though perhaps somewhat exaggerated) nevertheless reveals a humiliating phase in the history of British medicine. Charges of ignorance, dishonesty, and extortion were provoked on both sides; the dispensarian physicians accused their brethren of the opposite camp of playing corruptly into the hands of the apothecaries by prescribing enormous and unnecessary quantities of medicine. But there were other indications that medicine was passing through one of its less creditable periods, as ethical standards of practice left much to be desired. Doctors often inserted details of the patients they had successfully treated in the daily papers; medical pamphlets were written solely to impress the lay public with the author's professional skill; and hospitals and locks were built, under the guise of charity, by friends of a physician in order to establish his practice and make his name better known.

It is not quite certain how long Thomas Dover continued in his dual role of farmer and country physician. At the beginning of 1696 his father died, and apart from small bequests of five pounds to his elder son and daughters, the whole of his property passed to the physician.

Shortly after his father's death, Dover left his farms under the care of tenants, and settled in Bristol where he was appointed honorary physician to St. Peter's Hospital. Johnson records in his *Transactions of the Incorporation of the Poor* that Dover was the " first medical man who gratuitously offered his services on behalf of the poor, under the care of the guardians to this city in 1696 ".[2]

---

[1] *The Works of Alexander Pope*, New ed., 1871, Vol. II, 39.

[2] JAMES JOHNSON, *Transactions of the Corporation of the Poor in the City of Bristol*, 1826, 108.

The workhouse hospital, with which Thomas Dover was associated, was at that time a unique social experiment in the provinces. It resulted from the efforts of John Carey, who formed the Incorporation of the Poor in order to relieve the increased poverty resulting from the French war, which had seriously depressed the local weaving industry. Formerly each parish had been responsible for supporting its own paupers by means of a parish poor rate, but following the sudden increase of paupers each parish was anxious to evade the additional burden of supporting many more poor people.

Carey proposed a common fund and a single workhouse for the whole city. His scheme was confirmed by Act of Parliament in 1696. Thus the Bristol Poor Law Act became the first of its kind in the country, until a few years later many other places also applied to Parliament for similar powers. Several of their Poor Acts were copied from Bristol, with little or no alteration. The governing body (called the " Incorporation of the Poor ") set up a central workhouse in which able-bodied paupers might be housed and compelled to work, the infirm economically maintained, and the young trained to be fitted for a life of honest labour and " not to be brought up in the manner of vice as they now are ".[1]

The City Aldermen elected four representatives to serve as Guardians to the Incorporation. They purchased a building (formerly the Royal Mint) which was used partly as a hospital and partly for the spinning of cotton : it was at this institution, later known as St. Peter's Hospital, that Thomas Dover practised. In another house, called Whitehall, a hundred girls were employed in carding and spinning wool. But the project, so far as the Guardians were concerned, was not entirely altruistic, as by these means they hoped to establish a large manufacturing trade of woollen and cotton cloths from which great profits were expected. Though their financial expectations proved vain, the Guardians continued to pursue a rigorous policy designed to increase production and reduce costs. Discipline was rigidly enforced ;

---

[1] JAMES JOHNSON, *Transactions of the Corporation of the Poor in the City of Bristol*, 1826, 28.

special badges had to be worn on the outer garments of all paupers.; and two iron chains with locks attached were purchased for the purpose of fastening disorderly inmates in a special section of the hospital suitably known as " Purgatory ". A pair of stocks and a whipping post were also erected in the courtyard.

At the start of this venture there were financial difficulties with some of the staff. Two years after they had been appointed the surgeons were granted ten pounds per annum for their attendances ; but in 1703 they all resigned following a dispute for a higher pay. Messrs. Sandford and Deverell were shortly afterwards reappointed at the joint salary of £32 per annum, together with Mrs. Dagg, a midwife, who was instructed to call a surgeon only for difficult deliveries. It was added that the surgeons were at liberty to attend any female patient in hospital (should they so desire) as Mrs. Dagg's appointment was merely to save them unnecessary work.

Ringworm seems to have taxed the skill of physicians and surgeons, and Mrs. Case was granted five shillings for curing " scruffy heads ". Also Mary Carter, aged seventy, was employed " to pick cotton and look after the boys' heads ".[1] A special fee was granted to Mr. Godfrey, a surgeon, for curing " the broken belly "[2] of a man who had lifted a heavy weight.

There is no record of any fees paid to Dr. Thomas Dover, although he doubtless gained considerable clinical experience by attending the sick and ill-nourished paupers, at a time when charity was uncommon and the social services were just beginning.

---

[1] JAMES JOHNSON, *Transactions of the Corporation of the Poor in the City of Bristol*, 1826, 22.
[2] *Ibid.*, 127.

CHAPTER V

BRISTOL PHYSICIAN

Too much in turtle Bristol's sons delight,
Too much o'er bowls of rack prolong the night.

BYRON

AT the end of the seventeenth century, Bristol, with a population of roughly thirty thousand, was the leading British seaport, and in other respects ranked second to London in importance. Pepys, who visited Bristol eight years after the Restoration, was struck by the splendour of the city. He remarked on the peculiar feeling of being in a town (other than London) which was so packed with houses that the surrounding countryside was blotted out.

The only approach to the city was through the gates of Redcliffe, Temple, Newgate, and the rest, which led into a maze of narrow streets that had undergone little change throughout the centuries. As the streets of the old city were too narrow for wheeled traffic, goods were transported by packhorses, and wealthier citizens travelled on horseback. Even the busiest thoroughfares were under twenty feet across, and the common practice of overhanging upper stories further diminished the space between houses. There were no footpaths for pedestrians, and owing to the ceaseless passage of trucks and sledges called 'geehoes' (the only vehicle permitted in the centre of the city) the roadways were so slippery in wet weather as to be a frequent cause of accidents. A picturesque old bridge spanned the river, and between double rows of houses lining the bridge, streams of traffic poured in and out of the city. The muddy tide surged backwards and forwards twice a day in the Avon and Frome, into which rivers (with supreme indifference to sanitation) poured the contents of the city sewers. At ebb tide, women of the poorer class were to be seen washing at special sites along the banks.

Pope gives a vivid description of Bristol's waterfront during Dover's time :—

You come first to Old Wells, and over a bridge, built on both sides like London Bridge, and as much crowded, with a strange mixture of seamen, women, children, loaded horses, asses, sledges with goods, dragging along all together, without posts to separate them. From thence you come to a key (sic) along the old wall, with houses on both sides, and in the middle of the street as far as you can see, hundreds of ships, their masts as thick as they can stand by one another, which is the oddest and most surprising sight imaginable. The street is fuller of them than the Thames from London Bridge to Deptford, and at certain times only, the water rises to carry them out ; so that, at other times, a long street, full of ships in the middle, and houses on both sides, looks like a dream.[1]

As well as being a great port, Bristol had many industries. In the poorer thoroughfares the discordant sounds of smiths, coopers, braziers, joiners, and weavers prevailed : and wayfarers were regaled with the pungent odour of the soap-boiler, the tallow chandler, and the dyer. A picturesque feature of the times (due to illiteracy rather than taste) was the galaxy of colourful designs, such as lions, eagles, elephants, and tigers, suspended from the shop fronts in order to catch the pedestrian's eye and indicate the type of business within.

It was a time of violence, when malefactors were punished with great brutality. One of the barbarous customs of the age was to brand the cheek of people convicted of petty theft. This practice, performed in open court, was so repugnant to the feelings of the more sensitive officials as to lead to evasions of the law. In one case a Bristol sheriff was fined £2 for not causing two women to be " well burnt ".[2] Frequently prisoners bribed the brander to apply his irons cold ; but the cruel and wily old magistrates detected such ruses by insisting on seeing the smoke arising from the singed skin of each offender.

A woman found guilty of fraudulently obtaining three yards of cotton was sentenced to be stripped to the waist, and whipped down one side of High Street and up the other. For

---

[1] *The Works of Alexander Pope*, New ed., 1886, Vol. IX, 326.
[2] JOHN LATIMER, *Annals of Bristol in the 18th Century*, 1893, 69.

stealing a cheese a man was ordered to be flogged from All
Saints Church to the White Horse Inn, Redcliffe Street, and
from there back to Newgate, the cheese to be carried at his
side. Moral offenders were exhibited as objects of public
ridicule. By an ancient custom of the City people convicted
of lewdness were set backwards upon a horse and paraded
about for the delectation of the multitude. Women found
guilty of common scolding were tied into a ducking stool
which was then plunged into the Frome amidst jeering
acclamations.

The basis of Bristol's prosperity was, of course, the maritime
trade. Bristol merchants had been the first to develop
commerce with North America and the West Indies.
According to Barrett seventy Bristol ships were employed in
the West Indies trade alone. " Before the Civil War there
was a great foreign trade, especially to the West Indies, but
since the Revolution the trade to North America and
Newfoundland, to Guinea, the Mediterranean, to Norway,
Hamburgh and up the Baltic has been greatly improved and
extended. They have buyers at home for the largest cargoes ;
whence the shopkeepers in Bristol derive a great inland trade,
being wholesale dealers throughout the Western countries,
which employs a great many carriers and wagoners passing
and repassing from Bristol to the principal towns."[1]

Wealthy Bristol merchants were famous for their love of
display. At the baptism of their children, and even more so
at the funerals of their relatives, they were prone to indulge
in costly parade. Funerals were ceremonial occasions and
usually took place about midnight. The coffin was borne
along the streets with all the attendant pomp of escutcheons,
sconces, candles, flambeaux, plumes, and mutes : the tolling
of the parish bell at such an hour would cast the neighbourhood into gloomy reflections on the transience of mortal
life.

Sea captains, particularly those engaged in the lucrative
occupation of slaving, preferred to flaunt their wealth in
extravagant apparel. They wore cocked hats, gaudily laced

---

[1] WILLIAM BARRETT, *History and Antiquities of City of Bristol*, 1789, 184.

PLATE 1

St. Peter's Hospital, Bristol.
(*By courtesy of British Railways.*)

PLATE II

Crossing the Tropic; sailors being ducked at the yard arm.
(From a scarce print in the Macpherson Collection.)

coats and shoes with engraved gold buckles. They were frequently attended by a black slave who obsequiously trotted a few paces behind. Thus Bristol was a flourishing city when Dr. Dover settled there. As well as numerous wealthy merchants, there was also a large and affluent middle class of small tradesmen, shopkeepers, and others engaged in the ancillary occupations of a great seaport in which increasing profits were gained from such rapidly developing industries as weaving, glass manufacture, dyeing, and spinning.

Yet in spite of the size and prosperity of Bristol it is surprising that there were so few physicians; hence medical practice must have been highly rewarding. Even forty years after Dover had left Bristol there were only five physicians, nineteen surgeons, thirteen barber-surgeons, and twenty-nine apothecaries practising there. Physicians' fees were one guinea a visit, a sum which aroused envious comment from the clergy, whose stipends only amounted to between £30 and £100 annually. The Bristol clergy complained that the citizens did not " think a physician overpaid for one guinea a visit but expect to receive a year's service from a clergyman for five pounds".[1]

Following his honorary appointment at the hospital there can be little doubt that Thomas Dover soon acquired an extensive practice amongst the rich merchants and tradesmen. When he first settled in Bristol most of the doctors lived in St. James Barton, but later Queen Square, where Dr. Dover built one of the first houses, became more fashionable.

It was from here that he set out on his daily calls dressed in a manner that was then pathognomonic of the physician. A three-cornered black hat covered his wig, and a velvet suit, usually of a sombre hue and suitably dignified with ruffles and lace, was partly covered with a voluminous red cloak, called a roquelaure. A French rapier was often carried, but a more constant sign of his office was a professional cane, in the ornamented knob of which was a vinaigrette to hold near his nose when entering a sick room, in order to ward off infection. No doctor of medicine would presume to pay a

---

[1] H. J. ORR-EWING, *Bristol Med.-Chir. J.*, 1950, **67**, 5.

4

professional call without his mystic cane, which was said to be
a symbolic survival of the wand of Æsculapius.

After his morning visits, Dr. Dover would return to the
West India Coffee House, where the " bitter black drink ", as
Pepys called it, was served to all who wished to transact
business, read the newspapers, or merely rub shoulders with
their fellows. Situated in the market place, it was a favourite
haunt of Bristol medical men ; the barber-surgeons had their
guild room there, and between certain hours Dr. Dover
would also be available for consultation with his apothecary.
Minor ailments were usually treated by the apothecaries
without reference to a physician ; and judging from the
incredible amount of medicines sold by Bristol apothecaries
it would appear that the eighteenth century had just as much
faith in a bottle of physic as the present generation. One
Bristol family paid £350 in three years for various medicines ;
and Brodering, a Bristol apothecary, is said to have made
£4000 per annum from the direct sale of drugs rather than
from physicians' prescriptions.

Only in more serious illnesses would the apothecary resort
to a coffee-house and discuss the particulars of the case with a
physician. Hence physicians rarely saw the patients they
treated. Wealthy families would usually insist on the attendance of a physician, but the majority of people only seemed
to call him on a domiciliary visit when their relative was *in
extremis*. Indeed it was complained in Bristol that physicians
" came only to administer musk and to close the eyes of the
patients ".[1] Contemporary newspapers give an indication of
the cost of a physician's prescriptions. A bottle of medicine
cost twelve shillings, the draught one shilling and sixpence, and
musk was ten shillings and sixpence ; yet in spite of the expense,
most families bought musk so that their relative might die
amidst a comforting aroma of sanctity.

As well as the orthodox bottle of medicine, many wealthy
patients sought health from the Bristol 'Hotwells',[2] a fashionable therapeutic Mecca in Dover's time. An apothecary

---

[1] W. H. HARSANT, *Bristol Med.-Chir. J.*, 1950, **17**, 301.
[2] J. UNDERHILL, *Thermalogia Bristoliensis*, 1703.

called Underhill extolled the virtue of this well-water in a whimsical dissertation called *Johannis subteraintani Thermalogica Bristoliensis*, in which he cited a great number of instances in which sufferers from various maladies (including a diabetic cured in thirteen weeks) had been restored to health by taking the waters. In order to enhance the social appeal a list of titled patients who had benefited was also appended. The mystical healing powers of "a king by divine right" were still invoked whilst Dr. Dover was honorary physician to St. Peter's Hospital. Twelve patients suffering from the King's Evil (cutaneous tuberculosis) were sent from St. Peter's Hospital to Bath in order to be touched by Queen Anne. She was the last of a long line of sovereigns from the time of Edward the Confessor who exercised the royal gift of healing. William III did not ' touch ', but instead gave money to charity. But Anne as a legitimate monarch, and a Stuart to boot, continued to exercise the curative power of kings. This must have been one of the last occasions when royal treatment was available, as the ceremony ceased when she died.

Thomas Dover's Bristol residence was a period of intense professional activity. Most of his time would be spent in travelling the city; first, to attend his private patients, and then to the coffee-house, and later to St. Peter's Hospital. Preventive medicine was then unknown ; overcrowding, bad sanitation, faulty water supplies, and poverty all predisposed to frequent epidemics. Dire poverty inevitably led to typhus. One such epidemic of ' the spotted fever ' broke out with particular severity whilst Dover was on the staff of St. Peter's, and judging from the number of patients he treated daily it must have taxed his energy and resource to the utmost. " About fifty years since the fever raged so much in Bristol ", he says, " so that I visited from twenty-five to thirty patients a day for a considerable time, besides their poor children taken into the work-house, where I engaged myself for the encouragement of so good and charitable an undertaking, to find the physick, and give them advice at my own expense and trouble, for the first two years. All these poor children in general had this fever, yet no more than one died out of the whole number, which was near two hundred."[1]

It is a pity that Dover does not give the details of his treatment of typhus—a fever of grave prognosis. Assuming this account to be true, and the diagnosis correct, then we can only conclude that his results were exceptional, and his treatment was highly effective. Although his contemporaries were sceptical of Dover's statement, it is of interest to note that his figures only relate to the treatment of children, in whom it is now known that the prognosis is considerably better than that of adults.

However, Dover does give an account of his treatment of typhus in an adult, after more orthodox measures had failed.

I shall give a particular instance of one person cured in an uncommon way. One Thomas Hackett, an apprentice to Mr. John Scandrett, a grocer in Wine Street, Bristol, labouring under this fatal fever, had a violent hæmorrhage, or flux of blood at his nose, notwithstanding great quantities of blood were taken from his arms, and the most cooling medicines adminis-tered which could be thought of ; yet all proved ineffectual in so much that there was no room to expect his life. I ordered a large vessel to be filled below stairs with spring water. He was carried down in a sheet and put into the water. He dipped his head several times, upon which the bleeding stopped. I believe he might continue in the water a quarter of an hour, after which time he was carried to bed only covered with a sheet. He slept well that night, the spots all disappeared, he was very well, only weak, and is now living in Bristol.[2]

These heroic measures indicate that Dover was following Sydenham's cooling method to the extreme degree. Again he aroused the scepticism of his contemporary physicians. Dr. Turner writes that he met a Bristol man in a London coffee-house who knew Dover's patient quite well. From this indirect and somewhat dubious source of information, Turner then states that the patient denied ever suffering from ' spotted fever ' and that the epistaxis for which Dover treated him was probably due to scurvy.

Evidently this cold water treatment was then in vogue, as Mr. Bradley, who also ridicules Dover's claims, gives the

---

[1] THOMAS DOVER, *The Ancient Physician's Legacy*, 1742, 6th ed., 107.
[2] *Ibid.*, 108.

details of another patient who died as a result of similar treatment. Of the doctor who attended him he writes :—

He was unwilling to lose him for two Reasons ; First, he had a good Respect for the Man : In the Second place he owed him seventy pounds, which he had lent him in an Emergency, and not willing to lose his Money, he prevail'd upon the Patient's Friends to submit him entirely to his Management, which they accordingly did. He order'd him to be brought down in a Sheet, was put into a Tub of cold water ; several vessels being already filled for the purpose, were emptied over his Head and Shoulders, was afterwards carried to Bed ; but the poor Patient died before Night, and the Apothecary lost his Money, besides some Reputation for so imprudent an Action.[1]

During the year 1702 Thomas Dover was on the threshold of a new phase of medical practice. His hospital appointment brought him into contact with the governors of the " Incorporation of the Poor ", the majority of whom were wealthy merchants. Also at the West India Coffee House (in addition to his medical colleagues) he would meet sea captains, ship owners, merchants and representatives of every trade that serves a thriving seaport ; their talk would be of cargoes, the movements of ships, and strange lands.

Bristol trade to the West Indies had recently been given a further stimulus by the abolition of the monopoly granted to the Africa Company which had hitherto been entirely controlled by London merchants. For many years Bristol merchants had complained of the restrictions on the slave trade which favoured the Africa Company ; but as soon as this monopoly ended, they lost no time in carrying cargoes to Africa, where their merchandise was bartered for human beings, who were transported to the West Indies. The ships then returned to Bristol loaded with tropical commodities. In 1709 Latimer states that the Bristol slaving trade was so flourishing that fifty-seven ships were in constant service.

Thomas Dover, who had become well acquainted with merchants, captains, and ship owners trading to the West Indies, visited these islands in 1702. Although Dover spent six years voyaging between Bristol and the Caribbean the exact nature of his employment is not fully known. He

---

[1] H. BRADLEY, *Physical and Philosophical Remarks on Dr. Dover's Late Pamphlet*, 1733, 106.

certainly practised medicine during this period, as many years later when writing on diabetes, he mentions " Mr. Jonathan Keate, later surgeon to the hospital of King's Town in Jamaica, who was so far gone in diabetes that he was not able to get out of his cabin. . . . I was on board with some Company who told me the surgeon of the ship lay dangerously ill and desired to see me. . . . I soon perceived his distemper and sent him from shore what I thought proper. In three or four days he came to Port Royal, to return thanks for the great service I had done him. . . . This is thirty years since."[1]

Judging from the large capital he possessed at the termination of these ventures it is virtually certain that his role was more remunerative than that of ship's doctor. Indeed, the Rev. Thomas Mangey (chaplain to the Bishop of London) when writing on Dover's method of treating small-pox describes him as a man " who hath been a sea-captain for many years, and who pretends to have learnt the method of cure in the West Indies where no one is known to die of the small-pox ".[2] However it would be unlikely for a physician to be appointed captain of a trading vessel unless he had a financial interest in the enterprise. Therefore a probable explanation is that Thomas Dover gave up his practice in order to join his merchant friends in fitting out a vessel (possibly a slaving ship) on which he served in the dual role of captain and doctor.

Whilst ashore in the West Indies, Thomas Dover proved to be an acute medical observer. He noticed that patients with the indigenous type of " small-pox " rarely died, which was in marked contrast to the high mortality rate from the disease in Great Britain. This difference was due to the fact that alastrim, and not true small-pox, was endemic in the West Indies. Dover, who was unaware of the difference in virulence between these two diseases, thought that the much higher recovery rate in the West Indies was due to a better form of treatment. This observation, followed as it was by a false conclusion, had a profound effect on his subsequent treatment of small-pox. His error is readily understandable. Apart from being milder than true small-pox, alastrim is in

---

[1] THOMAS DOVER, *The Ancient Physician's Legacy*, 1742, 6th ed., 28.
[2] JOHN NICHOLS, *Literary Anecdotes*, 1812, Vol. I, 135.

other respects clinically indistinguishable, and was regarded as true small-pox until 1865.

There is no doubt that these trading ventures, whatever their exact nature, were profitable, for in 1708 Thomas Dover was able to invest over three thousand pounds in a privateering voyage, and still retain his family land at Barton-on-the-Heath. He was then nearly fifty. Thus at a time when most men are contemplating a comfortable middle age, Thomas Dover gave up his Caribbean voyaging for the lure of even greater wealth, and adventure in privateering on " perilous seas in faery lands forlorn ".

CHAPTER VI

BIRTH OF A LEGEND

Charm'd magic casements, opening on the foam
Of perilous seas, in faery lands forlorn.

KEATS

THE expedition to the South Seas which Dr. Thomas Dover helped to finance, and in which he was destined to play a leading role, was in no sense a buccaneering adventure or a piratical cruise. Adventure there was in abundance; but neither the origin, nature, nor exploits of this voyage could be described as piracy. Many writers have distorted this aspect of Dover's career: around him has been cast a savage and flamboyant legend which does ill justice to the man, and ignores the temper of his times.

As a result of his association with this privateering voyage Thomas Dover has been variously labelled " a buccaneer ",[1] a " mountebank ",[2] a " pirate on the Spanish Main ",[3] and a " merchant adventurer ".[4] They are all inaccurate descriptions. The expedition was certainly not a trading voyage, as the two frigates were well armed and carried no merchandise: instead, the commander possessed a privateering commission granted by Prince George of Denmark, consort of Queen Anne, and Lord High Admiral of Great Britain and Ireland. This commission clearly laid down the object of the voyage, which was " to cruise on the coasts of Peru and Mexico, in the South Seas, against Her Majesty's enemies the French and Spaniards ".[5] Therefore, piracy and buccaneering are

---

[1] SIR WILLIAM OSLER, *Johns Hopk. Hosp. Bull.*, 1896, **7**, 1.
[2] L. ELOESSER, *Ann. Med. Hist.*, 1926, **8**, 31.
[3] L. DOPSON, *Warw. J.*, 1947, **2**, 214.
[4] J. A. NIXON, *Bristol Med.-Chir. J.*, 1909, **27**, 31.
[5] *Declaration of Letters of Marque (High Court of Admiralty)*, 26/13, fo. 66 d.

strong words to describe the expedition which Thomas Dover accompanied : terms which were refuted by the articles of the commission, granted by the highest naval authority in Britain.

There is a wide historical and operational difference between a buccaneering adventure and a privateering voyage ; though the dividing line between a pirate and a buccaneer was often rather shadowy. The former scrupled not from whom he would make his prize ; his was a lawless life, sailing without the cloak of a commission, and preying on shipping of any nationality in the hope of profiting thereby.

The buccaneers, on the other hand, were originally French and English cattle-hunters settled on the Island of Tortugo, near Haiti, whose hereditary enemy was the Spaniard. They had no particular cause to love humanity as they were mostly Europeans who had been sold into slavery on the West Indian plantations, where they were subjected to brutal discipline, and the rigours of a tropical climate. The buccaneers took their name from the word 'boucan'—a process of jerking meat over a smoky fire as practised by the natives of the Caribbees. They lived by hunting wild cattle in the forests of these islands, and were clad in blouses and shorts, often stiff from the gore of slaughtered cattle : it is said that these bloody vestments were never changed, but were worn as a proud uniform.

After the startling achievements of Pierre-le-Grand, who was one of the first buccaneers to plunder Spanish towns and shipping, the settlers realized that waging war against the Spaniards was a much quicker way of getting rich than cattle-rustling. Most buccaneers made some effort to equip themselves with official papers that would lend to their raids some show of legitimate warfare. But many of their documents ill bore scrutiny ; and, judging by Esquemeling's account, some of these commissions had been purchased in much the same manner as a fishing licence. "We showed him our commission, which was now for three years to come. This we had purchased at a cheap rate, having given for it the sum of ten ducats or pieces-of-eight. But the truth of the thing was that at first our commission was made only for the space of three months, the same date as the Frenchman's was ;

whereas amongst ourselves we had contrived to make it last for three years—for with this we resolved to seek our fortunes."[1]

At the beginning of the eighteenth century the buccaneers were no longer a power in the Caribbean. Some of their leaders, like Captain Morgan, who became the Deputy Governor of Jamaica, retired into respectability. Others led their men to new scenes of action, as a result of which buccaneering thinned out and ultimately disappeared.

To appreciate the circumstances which led to Dover's privateering voyage it is necessary to survey briefly the cardinal features of English naval policy during the preceding century.

Until the reign of Elizabeth I, the interests of Spain and England had not actually clashed. But following the restoration of Protestantism, the hatred of Spain, which had begun to develop during the reign of Mary, burst forth with renewed vigour. The religious differences arising from the Inquisition on the one hand, and the persecution of the Catholics on the other, had, together with Elizabeth's refusal to marry Philip II, all contributed to embitter the political controversy arising from the Spanish desire to exclude all foreigners from the New World.

But these rich Spanish possessions in America offered a tempting prize to the privateering instincts of an island race: thus the ' sea-dogs ', with the connivance of Elizabeth I, committed enormous depredations upon Spanish commerce. The exploits of Sir Francis Drake were typical of such times. The defeat of the Armada finally established English maritime supremacy ; and on the death of Elizabeth I England was truly the mistress of the seas. Although the Royal Navy had been nearly doubled, it had played but a minor role in the history of her reign, as nearly all the maritime triumphs had been due to private adventurers.

The accession of the Stuarts led to a change in maritime policy. James I and His Most Catholic Majesty Philip of Spain were very friendly ; hence privateering was discouraged.

---

[1] JOHN ESQUEMELING, *The Buccaneers and Marooners of America*, 1890, 226. Ed. H. Pyle.

Financial difficulties under the Stuarts also led to a decline of the Navy ; and the Dutch gained ascendancy on the seas.

Privateering did not revive to any great extent during the reign of William and Mary. The British government no longer connived to their benefit although at this time French privateers had become very active. During the war which terminated with the Peace of Ryswick (1697), four thousand two hundred English vessels fell a prey to French freebooters involving a total loss of £30,000,000.

Such was the state of maritime affairs when Anne ascended the throne and the War of the Spanish Succession began. The experience of the seventeenth century had shown that, except when hostile commerce was prodigiously rich, privateering could not flourish under existing law. Even during the reign of William and Mary, when the Crown reserved only one-fifth of the value of all prizes taken by private individuals, privateering still failed to revive.

Heroic measures were necessary to restore this maritime enterprise which had done so much during the reigns of Henry VIII and Elizabeth I ; so on March 26th, 1708, a new Prize Act was approved by Queen Anne. It was designated " an Act for the better securing the Trade of the Kingdom by Cruisers and Convoys, and for the Encouragement of Cruisers ".[1] This Act was a crucial point in the history of British privateering. It marks the close of the period of decline, and the opening of an era of intense activity.

Provision was made for the transfer of the entire interest in the prize to the owner of the privateer, together with a bounty ' pour encourager les autres '. " That from and after 26 March 1708, if any ship or ships of war, privateer, merchant ship, or any other vessel shall be taken in prize in any of Her Majesty's Courts of Admiralty, the flag officer or officers, commander or commanders, and other officers, seamen and others who shall be actually on board such ship or ships of war or privateers, shall after such condemnation have the sole interest and property in such prize or prizes."[2]

---

[1] *Statutes at Large*, Vol. IV, Ch. V, Anne, C. 13, Act 6, 83.
[2] *Ibid.*, 336.

Henceforth the Crown ceased to expect any direct benefit from privateering, but encouraged these adventurers for the indirect benefit which would accrue from enemy losses.

In the eighteenth century the international conception of the nature of war was quite different from the modern view. War was not waged by States but by Monarchs who stood in actual personal enmity towards one another. Therefore every subject of one belligerent state was the enemy of every subject of the rival state. The language of some of the seventeenth and eighteenth century manifestoes clearly gives sanction to private individuals to commit acts of violence against the enemy. Queen Anne's declaration of war in 1702 simply states, " All acts of war against France and Spain or their subjects ".[1] No distinction was made between acts of war committed by naval vessels or privateers. On the contrary it is quite evident that the Government not only encouraged privateering, but also sanctioned their acts of aggression as an important contribution towards the war against Spain.

Shortly after the Prize Act was passed, thirty prominent Bristol merchants helped to finance the voyage which Thomas Dover accompanied. Amongst them were many city dignitaries. Three of the subscribers had been (or eventually became) Lord Mayors of the city : Sir John Hawkins (1701), James Hollidge (1709), and Christopher Shuter (1711). Captain Philip Freake and Thomas Clements were Sheriffs ; and John Ramsey was the Town Clerk of Bristol. The cost of fitting out two frigates for a voyage to the South Sea was £15,078, which was realized by issuing two hundred and fifty-six shares of £103 10s. each. Thomas Goldney, a Quaker grocer, was the largest subscriber with thirty-six shares representing an outlay of £3726 ; and Dr. Thomas Dover was the next largest shareholder with thirty-two shares purchased for £3312. The *Duke* cost £1318 and a further £6880 was spent on equipment ; her consort the *Dutchess* was bought for £830, and a further £4160 was required to fit her out.[2]

---

[1] *Statutes at Large*, Vol. IV, Ch. V, Anne, C. 13, Act 5, 114.
[2] B. M. H. ROGERS, " Woodes Rogers Privateering Voyage, 1708–11," *Mariners Mirror*, 1933, **14**, 208.

Due to his considerable financial stake in the enterprise, Dr. Dover was appointed second captain aboard the *Duke*, captain of marines, chief medical officer, and President of the Council with a double vote in its affairs. Ships' articles were drawn up, stating in detail the organization of the expedition, the list of appointments and the rules for distributing prize money. The function of the Council, which was made up of the senior officers from both ships, was "To determine all Matters and Things whatsoever, that may arise, or be necessary for the general good during the whole voyage. In case of Equality Captain Dover is to have the double voice as President of the Council and we do accordingly order him to be President."[1]

During the reign of Charles II it had been a common practice to appoint army officers to high naval commands, although the actual navigation had been carried out by sailing masters. Even at the beginning of the eighteenth century the appointment of a physician to high command in a privateering voyage would not be regarded as extraordinary, as he was a large shareholder with previous seafaring experience. Nevertheless the rapid transition from medical practitioner to officer of a private man-of-war seems incongruous. Henceforth the title of doctor is discarded, and throughout the voyage our physician is referred to as Captain Dover. It was a more apt title, as his subsequent role was to be of a martial, rather than a medical, nature.

Judging by the number of appointments, the medical welfare of the ships' company seemed well provided for. There was John Ballet, rated Third Mate, but designated Surgeon should the occasion arise: he had previously been with Captain Dampier on his last unfortunate voyage round the world, and was a sort of double-barrelled practitioner (not uncommon in those days) prepared either to operate when the occasion demanded or to take over the watch in quieter times. The apothecary, Samuel Hopkins, was Dover's brother-in-law: in addition to his medical duties he was

---

[1] Capt. Edward Cooke, *A Voyage to the South Sea*, 1712, Vol. I, Introduction, 8.

appointed to act as Captain Dover's lieutenant on a landing party. John Vigor, a reformado, was appointed to act as Dover's ensign when ashore. James Wasse was the chief surgeon, Charles May his mate, and John Lancey, assistant surgeon, made up the medical complement.

Of the other officers, perhaps the best known was Captain William Dampier, former buccaneer, explorer, and author. For ten years he had cruised and raided in the Caribbean with the buccaneers : later he was commissioned by the Admiralty to command the *Roebuck* on a voyage of discovery to the South Seas. Unfortunately his ship was unfit to undertake such a long voyage, and sank in calm weather. As a result of the misfortunes of this voyage, Dampier was found guilty of "hard and cruel usage"[1] to members of his crew, for which offence he forfeited his pay, and was "found not to be a fit person to command a King's ship".[2] Whilst awaiting another vessel Dampier maintained himself by exhibiting a Javanese Prince, who was one of the first examples of tattooing seen in England.

Dampier's writings, which were widely read at the time of their publication, served to arouse British interest in the Pacific. These books, containing carefully kept navigational details of his voyages, show that he was a scientific sailor. Harrison's marine chronometer had not then been invented, and there were no tables or instruments to calculate accurately Greenwich dates. Yet Dampier and his contemporaries, relying largely on latitude and dead reckoning, seemed to have sailed round the world in an uncannily accurate way. The Bristol owners were well aware of Dampier's ability as a navigator ; and although they were loath to appoint him to high command they availed themselves of his unrivalled knowledge of the Pacific, by employing him as "sailing master and pilot in the South Seas".[3]

The commander was Captain Woodes Rogers, and it was largely due to his efforts that the expedition proved so great a success. Callander describes Rogers as "A bold, active, indefatigable officer, one that could not give up his opinion

---

[1, 2] JOHN MASEFIELD, *Introduction to Dampier's Voyages*, 1906, Vol. I, 5.

[3] CAPT. EDWARD COOKE, *A Voyage to the South Sea*, 1712, Vol. I, Introduction, 3.

too readily to others, and who was not to be flattered by other people giving up their opinion to him. He had been a large sufferer by the French and was naturally no great friend to that nation ; but his most singular quality, and that which indeed recommended him to the command, was a peculiar art he had of maintaining his authority over his seamen, and his readiness in finding out expedients in the most difficult situations."[1]

Woodes Rogers came from an old Bristol family, and shortly after his marriage to the daughter of Sir William Whetstone, Commander-in-Chief West Indies, he became a Freeman of the City of Bristol, and thus acquainted with the merchants who financed the voyage. He had long been impressed by the way in which France and Spain monopolized the whole trade to the South Seas, and was determined, if possible, to remedy this state of affairs. The war of the Spanish Succession, in which the forces of Great Britain, Austria, and Holland were allied against those of France and Spain, had lasted six years when Rogers realized that this would be a fitting and profitable opportunity to attack the enemies' commerce. " Necessity ", he says " has frequently put private men on noble undertakings."[2]

Captain Stephen Courtney, described as " a man of birth, fortune, and very amiable qualities ", was appointed commander of the *Dutchess*.[3] He had also contributed to the expense of the voyage. The second captain aboard the *Dutchess* was Edward Cooke, who had previously been the prisoner of a French privateer. " Most of us, the chief officers," writes Rogers, " embraced this trip of privateering round the world, to retrieve the losses we had sustained by the enemy."[4]

The rest of the crew were drawn from the many adventurers who frequented the taverns and coffee-houses of the Bristol

---

[1] JOHN CALLANDER, *Terra Australis Cognita*, 1768, Vol. III, 232.
[2] CAPT. WOODES ROGERS, *A Cruising Voyage round the World*, 1712. Cassell, 1928, 9.
[3] JOHN CALLANDER, *Terra Australis Cognita*, 1768, Vol. III, 232.
[4] WOODES ROGERS, *A Cruising Voyage round the World*, 1712. Cassell, 1928, 10.

waterfront. All that was required was a public notice
asking for " gentlemen sailors willing to serve on
board the ships *Duke* and *Dutchess* (privateers) to apply to the
captain ". It immediately brought forth an evil looking
bunch of city toughs, amongst whom were only a few
mariners. Every trade and nationality, as well as a fair
sprinkling of jailbirds, was amongst the volunteers.

> 'Tis true they were a lawless brood,
> But rough in form, nor mild in mood ;
> And every creed, and every race,
> With them hath found—may find a place.

The two ships were soon manned with this mixed crew of
landlubbers, and on August 2nd, 1708, they sailed from
King's Road, Bristol, bound for Cork in Ireland. The *Duke*
had a displacement of three hundred and twenty tons ; she
carried a crew of one hundred and seventeen, and mounted
thirty cannon. Her consort was a slightly smaller vessel of
two hundred and sixty tons, armed with twenty cannon, and
manned with a crew of one hundred and eight men. They
were both frigate built, a term which in those days referred
to a ship with a poop and forecastle rising a few steps above
the waist. Although very fast and easily manoeuvrable, they
were but slightly built for such an arduous voyage. Many a
modern pleasure yacht would exceed the tonnage of these
ships, as they measured only twenty-five feet abeam and
about eighty feet along the keel.

At Cork the two ships were provisioned, defective rigging
was repaired, and they were also careened and cleaned.
Whilst in Ireland Rogers took the opportunity of securing
some good seamen, making a total of three hundred and
thirty-four men. The proportion of officers was much
greater than normal for a privateersman—a wise safeguard
against mutiny or heavy mortality among them. Whilst the
two ships were weather-bound for three weeks the more
amorous aspect of a sailor's life was manifest in an epidemic
of marriages. Among others, a Dane married an Irishwoman,
neither understanding a word of the other's language, so that
they had to rely on an interpreter. " Yet ", says Rogers,
" I perceived this pair seemed more afflicted at separation

than any of the rest; the fellow continued melancholy for several days after we were at sea. The rest understanding each other, drank their cans of flip (a mixture of beer and spirit, sweetened with sugar, and heated) till the last minute, concluded with a health to our good voyage and their happy meeting, and then parted unconcerned."[1]

On September 1st the *Duke* and *Dutchess* left Cork for the Bay of Biscay. They were accompanied by twenty merchant-men, and convoyed by H.M.S. *Hastings*. Six days out from Ireland their naval escort returned, and the voyage began in earnest. Both ships were heavily laden with stores and overcrowded with a raw polyglot crew amongst whom were tinkers, tailors, haymakers, pedlars, and fiddlers, together with ten boys and one negro. The ships' mascot, a fine specimen of an English bulldog, tended to add a touch of the burlesque. Yet Rogers seemed confident of his crew, " with which mixed gang we hope to be well manned as soon as they have learnt the use of arms, and got their sea legs. After which ", he grimly adds, " we doubt not soon to teach 'em and bring 'em to discipline."[2]

Thus began one of the most successful privateering voyages in British maritime history. Though the diverse composition of its members had a strong Gilbertian flavour, yet, as they sailed into peril and high adventure, their spirits proved to have been cast in an Elizabethan mould.

---

[1] WOODES, ROGERS, *A Cruising Voyage round the World*, 1712. Cassell, 1928, 5.
[2] *Ibid.*, 6.

5

66

CHAPTER VII

THE RESCUE OF SELKIRK

There's nought, no doubt, so much the spirit calms,
As rum and true religion.

BYRON

It is difficult for us, nurslings of a softer age, to put ourselves in the old mariners' place; to picture the life and thoughts of those unlettered men, starving, or subsisting for weeks together on rotten meat and rum, flogged with a rope-end, sore and bloated with scurvy and the pox, scabrous with lice and the itch. The natural recourse of such men was to drink, for that made merry men of these poor tortured beasts. To see others suffer cannot have affected them much, for they were all constantly tormented; to see others die (as so often they had seen their shipmates die) of wanton cruelty, starvation, hardship, and disease was of but slight consequence to them. Their lives were violent, their times fostered great hardships, their bodies were plagued by foul distempers; these and other torments bred coarse, savage men, yet tough withal.

Very soon they were to get a taste of Rogers's stern rule. The two ships had chased and overhauled a vessel flying Swedish colours, believed to be carrying contraband goods. But as nothing was found to prove her a prize, Rogers let her go on her way after exchanging presents with the captain. His action was taken as a sign of weakness by the crew, who were incensed by the thoughts of plunder; and under the leadership of the boatswain of the *Duke* several of them mutinied. An ugly situation developed for which Rogers adopted harsh measures; ten of the mutineers were put in irons, one was flogged, others less guilty were punished and discharged. The senior officers were all armed, and kept together for fear of attack. The following day a sailor, supported by nearly half the ship's company, demanded that the boatswain be released ; Rogers immediately arrested the man and ordered him to be flogged by one of his friends. This forthright action broke up the mutiny, and some days later the men in irons, after begging forgiveness and promising no further trouble, were released.

Eighteen days out from Cork they passed Madeira and cruised among the Canary Islands in search of liquor, as Rogers was of the opinion that " good liquor to sailors is preferable to clothing ".[1] They were soon fortunate in capturing a small Spanish barque, carrying forty-five passengers, which they took to Oratava, where after some delay and a threatened bombardment of the town, the Spaniards ashore eventually agreed to the terms of ransom. The transaction ended satisfactorily, and the two ships sailed away " well-stocked with liquor, the better able to endure the cold when we get the length of Cape Horn ".[2]

It would appear from the next entry in the log that homage was paid to King Neptune before actually crossing the equator, at what the sailors call the ' Horse Latitudes '. On September 25th Rogers writes :—

We passed the Tropick and according to custom ducked those who had not done so before. The manner of doing it was by a rope thro' a block from the main yard to hoist 'em above half way up to the yard and let 'em fall at once into the water, having a stick cross thro' their legs, and well fastened to the rope, that they might not be surprised and let go their hold. This prov'd of great use to our fresh-water sailors to recover the colour of their skins, which were grown very black and nasty. Those that were duck'd after this manner three times were about sixty, and others that would not undergo it chose to pay half-a-crown fine ; the money to be levy'd and spent at a public meeting of all the ships' companies when we return to England. The Dutchmen and some Englishmen desir'd to be ducked, some six, some eight, ten and twelve times, to have the better title to be treated when they come home.[3]

Their next port of call was the Cape Verde Islands, where they wooded, watered, and bartered with the inhabitants for

<hr>

[1] WOODES ROGERS, A Cruising Voyage round the World, 1712. Cassell, 1928, 8.
[2] Ibid., 16.
[3] Ibid., 17.

fresh provisions. On the eve of sailing Captain Dover presided at a most important meeting of the Council, when the distribution of any future plunder was decided upon by rank. An agreement was reached whereby each man was to receive the following share : a sailor or landsman ten pounds ; any officer below carpenter twenty pounds ; a mate, gunner, boatswain or carpenter forty pounds ; a lieutenant or master eighty pounds ; and the captains one hundred pounds, over and above the gratuity promised by the owners to such as rendered outstanding service. It was also agreed that Captains Rogers and Courtney should have an extra five per cent ; and that a reward of twenty pieces-of-eight would be given " to him that first sees a prize exceeding fifty tons ".[1] This agreement was ratified by officers and men of both ships, before they weighed anchor and set a course for the Brazilian coast.

Stretching before them was the vast expanse of the South Atlantic and the pitiless wrath of the Horn. The skill and recourse of those master mariners seems extraordinary when one considers the meagre navigational aids at their disposal. They were venturing into almost unknown seas, with only a few charts (which subsequently proved to be inaccurate) and into an ocean that for more than two centuries had been dominated by the Spaniards. Their only navigational aid was Seller's *Practical Navigation*, published in 1614, and their standard instrument was " Davis's Quadrant ", a relic from Elizabethan times.

But in spite of these handicaps the two ships made an uneventful voyage to the Island of Grande, off the Brazilian coast. Rogers records that the first man ashore was Captain Dover, who set out on a shooting trip with one or two of the other officers, whilst the sailors began to career the ships. Presently he returned with " a monstrous creature, having prickles or quills like a hedgehog, with fur between them, and the head and tail resembled those of a monkey. It stunk intolerably, which the Portuguese told us was only the skin ; that the meat of it was very delicious, and they often kill'd

---

[1] WOODES ROGERS, *A Cruising Voyage round the World*, 1712. Cassell, 1928, 23.

them for the Table. But our men, being not yet at very short allowance, none of 'em had stomach good enough to try the experiment : so that we were forced to throw it overboard, to make a sweet Ship."[1]

Whilst at anchor off the Island of Grande, two Irishmen tried to desert the ships, but night came upon them whilst making their way through the thickly wooded country in the interior of the island. They panicked at the sounds of baboons (which they thought were tigers) and made haste to rejoin their ship, where they were flogged and put in irons.

French pirates had operated for some time along the coast to the depredation of the local inhabitants, and at first the Brazilians were suspicious of the new arrivals. However, on learning that they were British, the principal officers were welcomed by the Governor and friars who treated them very well. On the Governor's invitation the ships' companies assisted at a religious function. Ten officers and two trumpeters provided the British contingent at a church service, during which they played such inappropriate tunes as " Hey, boys, up go we ". Afterwards the trumpeters, who by this time were more than half drunk, marched at the head of the company. Then followed an old priest and two friars carrying lamps of incense ; an image decorated with flowers and wax candles ; forty more priests and friars ; and finally the procession was completed by the Governor, Captains Rogers, Courtney, and Dover, each carrying a long lighted candle.

After the ceremony they were splendidly entertained by the priests at their monastery and later by the Governor. Before sailing Rogers returned their hospitality aboard the *Duke*, where, he says, " They were very merry, and in their cups proposed the Pope's health to us. But we were quits with them by toasting the Archbishop of Canterbury ; and to keep up the humour William Penn's health, and they liked the liquor so well, that they refused neither."[2]

Early in December the two ships bade farewell to the Island of Grande, and commenced their long and arduous

[1] WOODES ROGERS, *A Cruising Voyage round the World*, 1712.   Cassell, 1928, 29.
[2] *Ibid.*, 32.

voyage around Cape Horn to the Island of Juan Fernandez, a distance of nearly six thousand miles. They soon ran into foul weather. Three days out, Rogers records the sighting of an albatross which came out of the mist across the bow of his ship.

The weather became colder. At times the two ships lost touch with one another in the fog ; and for the first time since leaving England the *Duke*'s mainsail was reefed. The monotonous sea life wore on ; day after day the log records details of the weather, their course, and was only occasionally varied by such poignant entries as " In cold, hazy, rainy weather, one of the men aboard the *Dutchess* fell out of the mizzen-top, and broke his skull. Was beyond the help of the surgeons, died, and was buried next day."[1]

But in spite of the intense cold and strong gales the New Year was ushered in according to the custom of the sea. " A large tub of hot punch upon the quarter-deck, where every man on the ship had above a pint to his share, and drank our owners' and our friends' health in Great Britain. After which ", writes Rogers, " we bore down to our consort and gave him three huzzars, wishing them the like."[2]

The actual passage of the Horn is vividly described by Rogers in language that smacks of the sea.

On the fifth of January, just past noon, it came on to blow strong ; we got down our fore-yard and reefed our foresail and mainsail ; but there came on a violent gale of wind and a great sea. A little before 6 p.m. we saw the *Dutchess* lowering her main-yard. The tack flew up, and the lift unreefed, so that the sail to leeward was in the water and all aback, their ship taking in a great deal of water to leeward. Immediately they loosened their spritsail and bore her before the wind. I wore after her, expecting when they had gotten their mainsail stowed, they would take another reef in, and bring to under a two-reefed mainsail and reefed and balanced mizzen. But to my surprise they kept scudding to southward. I dreaded running amongst ice, because it was excessive cold ; so I fired a gun as a signal for them to bring to, and brought to ourselves again under the same reefed mainsail. They kept on, and our men reported an ensign in their main top-mast rigging as a signal of distress which made me doubt they had sprung their main-mast.

---

[1] WOODES ROGERS, *A Cruising Voyage round the World*, 1712. Cassell, 1928, 75.
[2] *Ibid.*, 78.

So I wore again, our ship working exceedingly well in this great sea. Just before night I was well up with them again, and set our foresail twice reefed to keep them company, which I did all night. About three the next morning it grew more moderate. We soon after made a signal, to speak with them, and at five they brought to. When I came within hail I enquired how they did on board. They answered they had shipped a great deal of water in lying by, and were forced to put before the wind, and the sea had broke in the cabin windows, and over their stern, filling their steerage and waist and had like to have spoiled several men. But God be thanked, all was otherwise indifferent well with them only they were intolerably cold and everything wet.[1]

The hardships of the voyage were now beginning to tell on the men ; some were down with scurvy ; and all of them were suffering from the intense cold from which their clothing afforded scanty protection. There was an urgent need to find a harbour where the sick might recuperate and the ships be overhauled.

With this object in view they set a course for the Island of Juan Fernandez, and after some difficulty in locating the island (as all their charts differed) they finally arrived there on the last day of January, 1709. That same afternoon a pinnace under Captain Dover rowed off towards the shore which was about four leagues away. Rogers was not inclined to allow the pinnace to set out for the shore at such a great distance ; but he finally yielded, in order to placate Dover, who always was most eager to be the first on land.

As the ship's boat was approaching the island (by which time it was dark) Rogers, from the deck of the *Duke*, suddenly saw a light blaze up from the shore. It had also been seen by Dover, who at once ordered his men to make haste back to the frigate. Believing a French squadron was lying at anchor, Rogers immediately ordered the decks to be cleared for action ; and at daybreak the two ships stood in to engage. But not a single sail was to be seen. A yawl, again commanded by Dover, accompanied by Mr. Fry and six armed men was then sent to reconnoitre, and, as they had not returned within a reasonable time, Rogers feared that they had been captured by a newly installed Spanish garrison.

---

[1] WOODES ROGERS, *A Cruising Voyage round the World*, 1712. Cassell, 1928, 78.

Eventually Dover returned " with a man clothed in goatskins who looked wilder than the first owners of them ".[1] He turned out to be Alexander Selkirk, a Scot, who had been alone on the island for four years after a dispute with his captain who had left him stranded there. Dampier knew Selkirk to be an excellent ship's officer and, on his recommendation, Rogers immediately engaged him as a mate aboard the *Duke*. It was Selkirk who had made the fire ashore when the two frigates had first put into the bay.

During his long stay on the island he had seen several ships pass by, but only two had previously anchored there. They turned out to be Spanish ships ; and rather than risk capture and subsequent torture at their hands, Selkirk had preferred the solitude of his island. He had, however, been seen by the Spaniards who pursued him, but he managed to elude them by climbing a tree. Rogers was amazed at Selkirk's appearance, and fully records the details of his arrival :—

He had with him his Clothes and Bedding, with a Firelock, some Powder, Bullets, and Tobacco, a Hatchet, and a Knife, a Kettle, a Bible, some practical Pieces, and his Mathematical Instruments and Books. He diverted and provided for himself as well as he could ; but for the first eight months had much ado to bear up against Melancholy, and the Terror of being left alone in such a desolate place. He built two Hutts with Piemento Trees, cover'd them with long grass, and lin'd them with the Skins of Goats, which he kill'd with his Gun as he wanted, so long as his Powder lasted, which was but a pound ; and that being near spent, he got fire by rubbing two sticks of Piemento Wood together upon his knee. In the lesser Hutt, at some distance from the other, he dress'd his Victuals, and in the larger he slept, and employ'd himself in reading, singing Psalms, and praying ; so that he said he was a better Christian while in his solitude than ever he was before, or than, he was afraid, he should ever be again.[2]

Selkirk had lived largely off crayfish and goats' flesh. His dexterity in catching goats prompted Rogers to employ him to replenish the ship's larders. Of Selkirk's prowess in goat hunting Rogers comments, " We had a Bull-Dog, which we sent with several of our nimblest Runners, to help him in catching Goats ; but he distanc'd and tir'd both the Dog and

---

[1] WOODES ROGERS, *A Cruising Voyage round the World*, 1712. Cassell, 1928, 91.

[2] *Ibid.*, 92.

the Men, catch'd the goats and brought 'em to us on his back."[1]
His diet had been supplemented by turnips and cabbages,
planted by members of Dampier's previous expedition ; and
there was also the fruit of the pimento trees.

His mode of life had been hard, so that before long his
shoes and clothes were worn out ; and " being forc'd to
shift without them, his Feet became so hard, that he run every
where without Annoyance : and it was some time before he
could wear Shoes after we found him ; for not being us'd to
any so long, his Feet swell'd when he first came to wear 'em
again".[2]

Shortly after his isolation on the island, Selkirk was prone
to fits of profound melancholia during which he had often
considered taking his life. But gradually, by occupying his
mind in various pursuits, his spirits became more buoyant.
Apart from the goats, the only other animals on the island
were innumerable rats together with an equally large number
of cats. Fortunately Selkirk was able to develop some
symbiotic harmony between them. " The Rats gnaw'd his
Feet and Clothes while asleep, which oblig'd him to cherish
the Cats with his Goats-Flesh ; by which many of them became
so tame, that they would lie about him in hundreds, and soon
deliver'd him from the Rats. He likewise tam'd some Kids,
and to divert himself would now and then sing and dance
with them and his Cats : so that by the Care of Providence
and Vigour of his Youth, being now about thirty years old,
he came at last to conquer all the Inconveniences of his
Solitude, and to be very easy."[3]

Selkirk's clothing was made from goatskins which he had
stitched together with the aid of a nail using wool from his
old stockings. Through disuse his pronunciation of English
was halting and difficult to understand. " At his first coming
on board us, he had so much forgot his Language for want of
Use, that we could scarce understand him, for he seem'd to
speak his words by halves. We offer'd him a Dram, but he

---

[1] WOODES ROGERS, *A Cruising Voyage round the World*, 1712. Cassell,
1928, 93.

[2] *Ibid.*, 93–94.

[3] *Ibid.*, 94.

would not touch it, having drank nothing but Water since his being there, and 'twas some time before he could relish our Victuals."[1] Captain Edward Cooke, second captain of the *Dutchess*, wrote a similar account of Selkirk's rescue.

During their stay in Juan Fernandez Selkirk kept the ships supplied with two goats a day. No doubt the poor, half-wild sailor enjoyed these last goat hunts before being confined to the routine duties of ship's officer. Rogers dubbed him the " Governor " or " Absolute Monarch "; and it is from his account that Cowper derived his famous poem. " The Governour (tho we might as well have nam'd him the Absolute Monarch of the Island) for so we call'd Mr. Selkirk, caught us two goats, which make excellent broth."[2]

After thoroughly overhauling the ships, reprovisioning, and resting the sick men, they sailed from Juan Fernandez on what was to prove the most hazardous stage of their voyage. In his role as captain of marines, Thomas Dover was to play a conspicuous part during their subsequent activities.

With the intention of intercepting Spanish shipping, the raiders cruised northwards off the coast of Chile and Peru. It was not long before the *Duke* and *Dutchess* swooped on their first prey, a small prize of sixteen tons, manned by two Spaniards and some Indians. Piloted by the crew of this prize they anchored between the islands of Lobas de la Mer, where the small ship was refitted, and relaunched as the *Beginning*. She was equipped as a privateer, with a spare topmast from the *Duke* and a new deck to which four swivel guns had been added. When manned by thirty-two men under the command of Captain Edward Cooke she proved a useful asset, as two days after sailing she captured another small prize, the *Santa Josepha*, of fifty tons, carrying a cargo of timber, coconuts, and tobacco. The latter prize was re-christened the *Increase*, and became the hospital ship to which all the sick men and a doctor were transferred, under the command of Mr. Selkirk.

---

[1] WOODES ROGERS, *A Cruising Voyage round the World*, 1712. Cassell, 1928, 94.
[2] *Ibid.*, 96.

The prisoners had informed their captors that the wealthy widow of the late Viceroy of Peru was shortly expected to embark aboard a man-o'-war for Acapulco, with all her possessions. They were also told that another stout vessel, with many passengers (including a bishop) and well laden with merchandise, was expected on its way from Panama to Lima. Spurred on by this heartening news, Rogers decided to spend as much time as possible cruising off Payta in the hope of intercepting these handsome prizes. They had not long to wait; for two days after leaving Lobas a sail was spied at daybreak. A pinnace was lowered, under the command of Mr. Fry, first lieutenant of the *Duke*, which succeeded in capturing the *Ascension* of five hundred tons. This vessel, built galleon-fashion with very high galleries, was laden with timber and dry goods for Lima.

She was taken over by Mr. Fry, whilst the small squadron lost no time in searching for the other vessel carrying the bishop, as Rogers was determined " to watch narrowly in order to catch his Lordship ". Accordingly the three privateers cruised along the coast of Payta, the *Beginning* skirting the coast, the *Duke* seven leagues to windward, and the *Dutchess* seven leagues to leeward. But there was no sign of a sail.

Whilst on the look out for the Spanish ship, a number of important conferences were held. At one of these sessions the chief officers agreed that Mr. Carlton Vanburgh, agent of the owners, be struck off the list of committee members for abusing Captain Dover, and also for threatening to shoot one of the seamen who had refused to carry a carrion-crow. At another, and much more important meeting, it was decided to attempt the capture of Guayaquil, then one of the important ports of Peru, and since the establishment of the independent state of Ecuador in 1811, the chief port of the latter. The following resolution was passed unanimously :—

At a Committee held on board the ' Duke '—Frigot.

We have consulted and examin'd sundry Pilots taken in Prizes, and had several Meetings on this Occasion, being provided with convenient Vessels to carry our Men, Guns, Arms and other Necessaries to Guiaquil : We resolve to attempt it, having also consulted the most secret way of managing our Attempts on it without discovery. We do approve and appoint Capt. Tho. Dover, Capt. Woodes Rogers, and Capt. Stephen Courtney, to command the Men designed to land in three equal Parties; except 21 Men with Capt. William Dampier and Mr. Tho. Glendall, who are to manage and take care of the Guns, Ammunition, Provisions, &c. which we agree to be lodg'd in a convenient place, as near as possible to the best Landing-place nearest the Water-side, in order to take care and help ship off the Effects that we may take in the Town; who are also to serve either Commander, where most wanted.

We leave the Management of this Expedition wholly to the prudent Conduct of the above Commanders, whom we heartily wish and desire to consult each other on all occasions, as to the most promising Method to succeed and keep our Designs secret; which is the only way to prevent the Enemies removing their Wealth, or giving us a vigourous Reception. This is our Opinion; in witness whereof we have set our Hands, the 12th of April 1709.[1]

Detailed regulations were drawn up governing the behaviour of the landing-parties; and also defining articles of plunder. Although everything portable seems to have been considered as such, it is amusing to read in a further order that the three Commanders, with their customary gallantry, resolved that money, and women's ear-rings, with loose diamonds, pearls, and other precious stones, should be excepted.

---

[1] WOODES ROGERS, *A Cruising Voyage round the World*, 1712.   Cassell, 1928, 113.

CHAPTER VIII

THE CAPTURE OF GUAYAQUIL

Seeking the bubble reputation
Even in the cannon's mouth.

As You Like It

THE two frigates now headed for Point Arena, at the estuary
of Guayaquil river, which was to be their base of operations.
Thirty-six miles upstream, on either side of the river were the
twin cities of Guayaquil with a population of two thousand
Spaniards, as well as many more Indians and negroes. They
were the largest shipbuilding ports in Peru, from which the
British had every reason to expect great wealth should their
venture prove successful.

Rogers had now given up hope of intercepting the ship
carrying the Spanish bishop, but as they approached Point
Arena a sail was sighted. Two pinnaces were precipitately
sent in pursuit, and as only slight resistance was expected,
their swivel guns were left behind. As soon as the two small
boats came within range, the Spanish vessel hoisted her
colours and opened fire. The commanders of the pinnaces
agreed that one should row to the bow and the other to the
stern of the enemy, and attempt to board her. But as they
approached, the Spaniards brought a gun right aft, together
with about twenty small arms. The fight began before the
boats could reach their agreed stations, and they were forced
to engage abeam, where the enemy had five guns mounted.
Again the two pinnaces tried to close with the enemy; but
in so doing they came under such a withering broadside of
cannon, partridge shot, and musketry, that they were forced
to disengage, and return to the frigate carrying two killed
and three wounded.

In this futile attack Captain Rogers's brother, Thomas Rogers, was killed. After a few shots had been fired across her bow by the *Dutchess*, the Spanish ship surrendered. Unfortunately the bishop, together with his long awaited gold plate, had disembarked ten days previously. Nevertheless, she was a rich prize heavily laden, and manned by fifty Spaniards and over a hundred negroes. She was renamed the *Marquis*, and after increasing her armament from twelve to twenty guns, proved a useful addition to the fleet. The same day another small prize was captured, now making a total of eight vessels, together with over three hundred prisoners to guard and feed. All the prisoners were placed aboard the frigates, whose commanders were ordered to remain at sea (undetected if possible) for forty-eight hours, and then rendezvous with the landing-party at Point Arena.

The assault party of over two hundred men then embarked in the ships' boats and began to row the thirty-six miles up the river to Guayaquil. At the end of the first day they reached a swampy island halfway to Puna, where they hid their boats in the mangrove swamps during the ebb tide. When the tide changed they again embarked and alternately rowed and then towed one another, in the hope that they might thereby be mistaken for driftwood. Towards evening of the third day the party reached the Island of Puna, where they anchored about a mile from the town.

It was decided to attack at dawn, but as they approached two Indians gave the alarm, whereupon many of the inhabitants carried off their valuables to the woods before the British could reach them. The Governor, together with twenty other Spaniards, was captured ; and, for fear that Guayaquil should be forewarned, Dover ordered all the canoes and barques in the river to be destroyed. Puna proved to be only a small town with a chapel and about thirty houses, where some of the seamen found sufficient liquor to become hopelessly drunk. The offenders were promptly flogged before the whole party in order to terrorize the onlookers against any similar behaviour.

After sacking Puna the raiders rowed on towards Guayaquil. Earlier they had failed to agree as to who should lead the attack

on the city. After another lengthy discussion, it was decided
that Captain Dover, commanding a company of landsmen,
should be the commander-in-chief during the first day, and
that Captains Rogers and Courtney, each commanding a
company of seamen, should relieve him on subsequent days.
Whilst hiding amongst the mangrove swamps, the party were
tormented by mosquitoes, so when night fell they were
glad to cast off.

At midnight they were abreast the town and preparing to
land, when from the top of an adjoining hill a blazing beacon
signalled their arrival. In the town itself church bells and
musketry fire warned the inhabitants of the imminent assault.
Whilst huddling together in the darkness of the river the
attackers overheard two Spaniards ashore discussing the
recent capture of Puna and the presence of a British attacking
force in Guayaquil river. It was then that the evils of divided
counsel fell upon them ; and the thrust of this poised attack
was ignobly spent in their leaders' petty dissensions.

Their impotence was due to a quarrel between Dover and
Rogers. The latter favoured an immediate assault whilst the
city was in a state of confusion ; whereas Dover, supported by
the majority of the officers, argued that it would be more
prudent to postpone landing ashore, where their presence had
already been detected. The dispute became heated ; voices
were raised, so in order to avoid giving away their positions,
they moved down the river to conclude their argument.
Rogers then urged an assault at dawn, but again Dover
opposed his suggestion on the grounds that the Spaniards,
being forewarned, would fiercely resist. Should heavy
casualties be sustained, then the whole future plans of the
expedition would be jeopardized. As an alternative, Dover
advocated that a trumpeter be dispatched ashore with proposals
to trade their captured cargoes ; should these proposals be
acceptable then the whole attack would be called off. Dover's
suggestion was put to the vote of the officers, the majority of
whom favoured attacking the town at dawn. They further
agreed that Dover should lead the attack as he had frequently
requested. But again Dover stifled their resolution by
refusing to take the responsibility for any losses that might

be sustained during the encounter. Viewed in the most
favourable light his behaviour in this dispute would seem over
cautious, if not actually cowardly. Yet unlike Rogers and
most of the other officers he was a large shareholder in the
enterprise and had much at stake. Also Dover was relying
to a large extent on Dampier's experience, from whom he
had been informed that the buccaneers never attacked a city
once it was alarmed.

Exasperated with the interminable dispute, Rogers writes,
" By these reflections, and some other people's indifference, I
had reason to doubt the consequences of attempting the enemy
with success, since we were so divided amongst ourselves ;
therefore at length I yielded to send two of our prisoners,
instead of a trumpeter, as Captain Dover first proposed."[1]

The prisoners were put ashore with orders to demand the
surrender of the town ; they were told to return within an
hour, otherwise the city would be attacked. Meanwhile the
landing-parties captured some barques in which the Spaniards
were attempting to sail up the river and spread the alarm.
Within the appointed time the prisoners returned together
with Captain Lecamps, who informed them that presently
the Governor would come to discuss terms.

All next day Dover and Rogers haggled with the Governor
of Guayaquil : at first they had visions of getting more profit
from selling back their negroes and captured cargoes than by
ransacking the town. As a preliminary they agreed to sell
cotton goods for 140 pieces of eight a bale ; but whilst still
negotiating a price for other merchandise the Governor
begged leave to go ashore in order to consult other merchants.
The three commanders then ordered the best possible fare and
entertainment to be prepared for his return. But their
expected guest did not arrive. Instead came a present of two
bags of flour, two sheep, two pigs, and some jars of wine and
brandy, with a message from the Governor stating that he had
been unable to see the merchants concerned, but would see
them the next day. Rather ominously the message also

---

[1] WOODES ROGERS, *A Cruising Voyage round the World*, 1712. Cassell,
1928, 124.

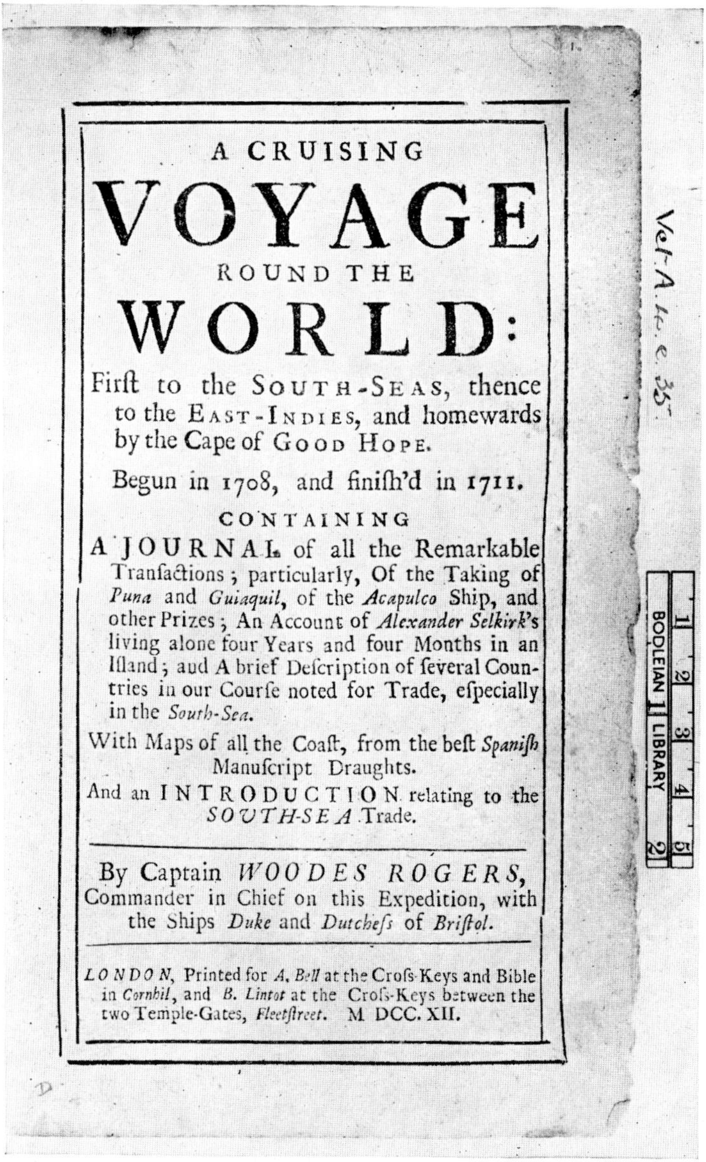

PLATE III

A CRUISING
VOYAGE
ROUND THE
WORLD:

First to the SOUTH-SEAS, thence
to the EAST-INDIES, and homewards
by the Cape of GOOD HOPE.

Begun in 1708, and finish'd in 1711.

CONTAINING

A JOURNAL of all the Remarkable
Tranfactions; particularly, Of the Taking of
Puna and *Guiaquil*, of the *Acapulco* Ship, and
other Prizes; An Account of *Alexander Selkirk*'s
living alone four Years and four Months in an
Ifland; and A brief Defcription of feveral Countries in our Courfe noted for Trade, efpecially
in the *South-Sea.*

With Maps of all the Coaft, from the beft *Spanifh*
Manufcript Draughts.

And an INTRODUCTION relating to the
SOUTH-SEA Trade.

By Captain *WOODES ROGERS*,
Commander in Chief on this Expedition, with
the Ships *Duke* and *Dutchefs* of *Briftol.*

LONDON, Printed for *A. Bell* at the Crofs-Keys and Bible
in *Cornhil*, and *B. Lintot* at the Crofs-Keys between the
two Temple-Gates, *Fleetftreet.* M DCC. XII.

Title-page of *A Cruising Voyage Round the World* by Captain Woodes Rogers.
(Bodleian Library.)

PLATE IV

Frontispiece of 1st edition of *Robinson Crusoe*.

Statue of Robinson Crusoe at Selkirk's birthplace of Largo.

added that although many more men had arrived in the town overnight he was still prepared to stand by the agreement. The Governor ended by imploring them not to attack the town, where many women and children were seeking sanctuary, as in any case they were poor with little or no wealth to plunder.

This message caused much uneasiness among the commanders, who, though they began to suspect some treachery, resolved to wait until the morning. At the appointed time the Governor and three other dignitaries came aboard carrying a flag of truce. A long series of discussions then began regarding the ransom price of Guayaquil. The British first proposed ransoming the town together with two ships and six barques anchored near the shore for 50,000 pieces of eight. Furthermore, after payment of this sum the Spaniards would be obliged to purchase the cargoes of two prizes together with all the negroes they had captured. The emissaries refused to agree to the British demands, and added that they had now sufficient men to defend the town. After a prolonged and heated argument the Governor offered 40,000 pieces of eight, which was accepted ; but before the agreement could be signed he again asked to go ashore to inform other citizens of his decision. Some hours later a messenger arrived to say that the inhabitants could only raise 30,000 pieces of eight. The messenger was told to return with an ultimatum that unless hostages for 40,000 pieces of eight were delivered forthwith the town would be attacked and no quarter would be given. Another half an hour passed. The messenger returned to inform them that only 32,000 pieces of eight could be raised. The patience of both Dover and Rogers was now exhausted, and they instantly ordered the flag of truce to be replaced by the Union Jack.

The Spaniards near the shore were told to keep away (if they valued their lives) whilst preparations were made for landing. Meanwhile two field guns weighing six hundred pounds were transferred to the ship's launch and rowed ashore. Captain Dover accompanied the artillery, whilst Rogers and Courtney led their companies of seamen ashore

6

in pinnaces.   To repulse the impending invasion, the Spaniards deployed their infantry along the houses leading to the quay (within half a musket shot of the British landing parties) and held their cavalry in reserve at the far end of the street.   Quite undaunted by this formidable array of soldiery who greatly outnumbered them the British clambered ashore ; and as each man landed, he fired from the knee, reloaded and advanced towards the enemy.   The advance continued ; they fired and reloaded so rapidly that the Spaniards had only time to discharge one volley before breaking their ranks and retreating. Likewise the cavalry galloped away to safety at the rear of the artillery.

The street led into a square, where the British came face to face with four Spanish guns preparing to give them a vigorous reception.   But again, at the first sight of this small attacking force, the Spanish cavalry retreated.   Their retreat encouraged the British sailors, who quickened the tempo of attack whilst directing their fire on the gunners and the crowds of soldiers immediately behind them.   As a result of the rapid and accurate British fire, the Spanish gunners had only time to fire one round of partridge shot (a charge of numerous missiles such as stones and pieces of iron), and before they could reload Captain Rogers and his men rushed the guns and captured them, together with twelve prisoners found hiding in a nearby church.   As none of the British was injured it would seem that the Spanish gunners were as inaccurate in aim as their cavalry had proved cowardly in their tactics.

Whilst Rogers secured the newly captured post at the church, Dover and Courtney chased the remnants to the out-skirts of the town ; and Dampier, now in charge of the captured artillery, completed the rout by directing their own guns on the retreating Spaniards.   Resistance soon ended ; and the different raiding parties established their headquarters in three churches whence they were able to dominate the whole town.   Dover's post was the most vulnerable, as the church he was occupying was dominated by a thickly wooded hill from where the enemy continued to fire on his party throughout the night.   As a counter measure, Dover ordered the houses in front of the church to be set on fire, which proved a wise precaution as during the night the enemy re-formed and attempted to storm his position.

It was indeed an eerie night for Dover's party. To protect themselves from the enemy's fire they remained inside the church, where, he says, they were very much annoyed with the smell of dead bodies that were decomposing under the loose floorboards. Outside, beyond the glare of the blazing houses, an invisible foe was ready to attack them at any unguarded moment. Rogers also remarks on the vulnerability of Dover's post. "The enemy", he says, "might have done him Mischief had they been courageous, since we were not near enough to assist him in the night. For the town being long, we could not keep the whole without dividing at such a distance; but his firing the houses covered the worst part of his quarters. Captain Courtney relieved him at daybreak, and they both quitted Captain Dover's quarters, as being too much exposed to the enemy."[1]

The search for plunder now began in earnest; but the victors of Guayaquil were very disappointed with the initial gains. Hearing from an Indian that the Spaniards had transported some of their gold up the river, a boat was sent to investigate. Meanwhile the town was ransacked; crowbars were used to break open church strongholds; cellar doors were ripped off, and in some cases walls were partly demolished. Some of the men were eager to tear up the church floorboards in order to continue their search amongst the corpses, but Dover forbade them, for fear of them becoming infected with the plague which had lately raged in the town :—

> Here the earth's breath is pestilence, and few
> But things whose nature is at war with life—
> Snakes and ill worms—endure its mortal dew.

This thorough ransacking of Guayaquil yielded large quantities of food, but few valuables, although in this respect the river party were more successful. After driving off a squadron of cavalry sent to relieve the city, they found a quantity of gold in the houses along the riverside. Rogers,

[1] WOODES ROGERS, *A Cruising Voyage round the World*, 1712. Cassell, 1928, 129.

with a customary show of gallantry, recounts the details of their search. "The houses up the river were full of women, and particularly at one place there were above a dozen handsome genteel young women well dressed, where our Men got several Gold-Chains and Ear-rings but were otherwise so civil to them that the ladies offer'd to dress 'em Victuals, and brought 'em a Cask of good Liquor. Some of their largest Gold Chains were conceal'd, and wound about their Middles, Legs, and Thighs, &c. but the Gentlewomen in these hot Countries being very thin clad with Silk and fine Linen, and their Hair dress'd with Ribbons very neatly, our Men by pressing felt the Chains, &c. with their Hands on the Out-side of the Lady's Apparel, and by their Linguist modestly desired the Gentlewomen to take 'em off and surrender 'em. This I mention as a Proof of our Sailor's Modesty, and in respect to Mr. Connely and Mr. Selkirk the late Governor of Juan Fernandez, who commanded this Party ; For being young Men, I was willing to do 'em this Justice, hoping the Fair Sex will make 'em a grateful Return when we arrive in Great Britain, on account of their civil Behaviour to these charming Prisoners."[1]

Emissaries were dispatched to treat for the ransom of the town, but they received only vague replies. Amidst many night alarms and occasional skirmishes during the day, the search for greater treasure continued. The Spanish Governor offered 30,000 pieces of eight to be paid within twelve days' time, but his offer was rejected by Rogers and Dover, as they suspected a design to prolong negotiations until the arrival of reinforcements.

Impatient with fruitless parley, Dover finally issued an ultimatum to the Spanish Governor, that unless an agreement was immediately signed the whole city would be set on fire that same afternoon. Within an hour the messenger returned with hostages for the city and the following flamboyantly-worded document was duly signed :—

Whereas the City of Guiaquil, lately in subjection to Philip V, King of Spain, is now taken by Storm, and in the Possession of the Capts. Thomas

---

[1] WOODES ROGERS, *A Cruising Voyage round the World*, 1712. Cassell, 1928, 131.

Dover, Woodes Rogers, and Stephen Courtney, commanding a Body of
Her Majesty of Great Britain's Subjects : We the underwritten are content
to become Hostages for the said City, and to continue in the Custody of
the said Capts. Tho. Dover, Woodes Rogers, and Stephen Courtney, till
30,000 Pieces of Eight shall be paid to them for the Ransom of the said
City, two new Ships, and six Barks ; during which time no Hostility is
to be committed on either Side between this and Puna. The said Sum to
be paid at Puna in six Days from the Date hereof, and then the Hostages
to be discharg'd, and all the Prisoners to be deliver'd immediately, otherwise the said Hostages do agree to remain Prisoners till the said Sum is
discharg'd in any other Part of the World. In Witness whereof we have
voluntarily set our Hands this 27th Day of April, Old Stile, and the 7th
of May, S.S. in the Year of our Lord, 1709.[1]

The agreement was signed without further ado ; the
hostages were transferred to the boats together with all
remaining plunder ; and with a final martial flourish the
victors, led by Captain Thomas Dover, marched through the
ravaged city for the last time, with drums beating and colours
flying. On the whole Rogers thought that the Spaniards
had got the better of them in this bargain. " For tho' upon
weighing Anchor at eight next morning from Guiaquil ",
he says, "we made what Show and Noise we could with our
Drums, Trumpets, and Guns, and thus took Leave of the
Spaniards very cheerfully, tho' not half so well pleased as we
should have been had we taken 'em by surprise. For I was
well assured from all Hands that at least we should have got
above 200,000 Pieces of Eight in Money, and a greater Plenty
of such Necessities as we now found."[2]

The plunder was not great ; about £1,200 in plate and
gold rings, one hundred and fifty bales of dry goods, four
guns, two hundred Spanish muskets, a few parcels of indigo,
cocoa, and about a ton of loaf sugar. During the engagement
only one man was killed (shot by his own sentry) and five
were wounded ; whereas the Spaniards lost fifteen killed and
wounded, including their chief gunner, an Irish soldier of
fortune.

The pinnaces uneventfully reached their rendezvous with
the *Duke* and *Dutchess* at Puna, after an absence of twelve days.

[1] WOODES ROGERS, *A Cruising Voyage round the World*, 1712. Cassell,
1928, 134.
[2] *Ibid.*, 136.

Whilst awaiting payment of the ransom, a ship was seen heading for Guayaquil river and after a short chase a barque of thirty tons was captured. She was heavily laden with flour, peas, beans, sugar, sweetmeats, and a large quantity of pomegranates, apples, and onions. Other ships were dispatched to Puna and returned loaded with livestock : thus at a crucial moment their stores were adequately replenished. At the appointed time a boat from Guayaquil arrived with 2200 pieces of eight in part payment of the ransom. They were told to return for the remaining money as the British privateers intended to sail with the morning tide ; indeed Captain Courtney was so eager to get under way that he sailed at midnight with Dover and Dampier on board. The next morning Rogers in the *Duke* collected the balance of payment in gold plate, weighed anchor, and set a course for the Galapagos Islands.

Whilst bound for these islands, a pestilential legacy from Guayaquil broke out amongst members of the crew who had been ashore there. About a month before the capture of the town, there had been an epidemic of plague, attended with a heavy mortality. For about five weeks an average of twelve Spaniards had died each day, and their corpses had been so carelessly buried that an odour of putrefaction pervaded the whole city. Dover diagnosed the fever as plague, and ascribed its cause to the malodorous atmosphere of Guayaquil. Some writers are sceptical as to the veracity of his diagnosis, but from the brief description in Dover's book it would appear that the epidemic was indeed plague. He says : " They all had spots which in the Great Plague they called Tokens, few or none of the Spaniards escaped death who had them but my people had them and buboes too."[1]

When they arrived at the Galapagos Islands, illness jeopardized the whole success of the voyage, as by that time over one hundred and eighty men were stricken with the plague. In his role of chief medical officer, Dover characteristically asserted himself. He ordered copious bleeding and abundant fluids, thus (according to his own account) only

---

eight patients died. These figures reveal a remarkably low mortality rate for plague, and again doubts have been expressed by Dover's contemporaries as to the veracity of this account. But the logs for the voyage kept by Rogers and Cooke record only thirteen deaths due to the plague of Guayaquil. Furthermore, as Dover was writing from memory over twenty years afterwards, his slight error is excusable. Amongst the early victims of the plague was Dover's kinsman Samuel Hopkins, the apothecary ; Captain Courtney was also taken ill and largely due to Dover's careful attention he recovered. But Rogers complained about the lack of medicines. " Our surgeons made heavy complaints for want of sufficient medicine ", he says, " for which, till now, I thought we abounded, having a regular physician, an apothecary, and surgeons enough, with all sorts of medicine on board. Our owners believed so too, and did often at home set forth the uncommon advantage we had on being so carefully provided for this tedious voyage ; but now we found it otherwise, and had not sufficient medicines to administer for the recovery of our sick men, which, so many being in both ships, makes it a melancholy time with us."[1]

Whilst cruising amongst the Galapagos two more small prizes were added to the fleet ; provisions were replenished with turtles and fish, but as water could not be found, they made for the island of Gorgona near the mainland. Whilst the sick were recovering all the ships were thoroughly over-hauled. In fourteen days the men caulked, careened, rigged, and stowed each ship ; their speed astonished the Spanish prisoners, who told Rogers that they usually took them about two months to refit. One of the prizes, the *Havre de Grace*, was fitted with a new mast, resourcefully fashioned from a tree on the island ; new sails and rigging were also fitted before she was re-launched, amidst great celebrations, as the *Marquis*.

Provisions were again at a low ebb. A meeting was held, and its resolution reveals Thomas Dover in another of his official roles—that of Captain of Marines.

[1] WOODES ROGERS, *A Cruising Voyage round the World*, 1712.   Cassell, 1928, 153.

Committee on board the ' Duke' riding at anchor in the Road of Gorgona,
July 9th, 1709.

We think it convenient to turn all our prisoners ashore in a bark already
provided for that purpose, and at the same time to plunder the settlements
on the main opposite to this island and do desire Captain Thomas Dover,
Mr. Robert Fry, and Mr. William Stratton to command the bark and
forty-five men on the same expedition, and to make what dispatch they
can, and return hither with such refreshments etc. as they could get for
our sick men.[1]

Rogers now began negotiating for the ransom of seventy-
two Spanish prisoners, who had all been well treated.
Religious tolerance (though not a strong characteristic of
those times) had been allowed them. " We allowed liberty
of conscience on board our floating commonwealth to our
prisoners ", writes Rogers, " for there being a priest in each
ship, they had the great cabin for their mass whilst we used
the Church of England service over them on the Quarter
Deck, so that the Papists here were the Low Church men."[2]

Dover returned from his foraging expedition with cattle,
pigs, goats, and fruit purchased from the mainland ; meat
supplies were further supplemented by shooting monkeys
which abounded on the island, and turtles kept up a supply of
eggs. Two Spanish prisoners, Captains Morel and Navare,
were ransomed together with their two ships and a large
quantity of captured cargo. As the British commanders
expected the next part of their voyage to be the most hazardous,
a document stressing the need for mutual co-operation between
the three ships was agreed upon and signed.

After leaving Gorgona, the squadron touched in at the
mainland for fresh provisions. At first, the coastal Indians
were afraid of them and ill disposed to trade. As a precaution
against possible attacks, half the men had to be kept under
arms whilst the ships were again refitted ; but eventually
Rogers gained the Indians' friendship by presenting three
Spanish saints to the chief, with a feathered cap for his wife.
Captain Dover's company of marines was further supplemented by the addition of thirty-five captured negroes who

[1] WOODES ROGERS, *A Cruising Voyage round the World,* 1712.   Cassell,
1928, 162.
[2] *Ibid.,* 165.

were drilled under Michael Kendall, a Jamaican. They were given names, clothing, firearms, and after intensive training they became a proud and reliable body of men, who were told to regard themselves as Englishmen, and no longer as Spanish slaves. Yet in some ways they were still regarded as ' prize goods ', for Rogers later records that it was agreed that Captain Cooke should have " the black boy Dublin, and Captain Robert Fry the black boy Emmanuel of Morineco as a free gift ",[1] in view of their outstanding services in capturing the *Marquis*. A few negresses were also captured, one of whom proved to be most undesirable, as shortly after their arrival on board " one John Edwards, a youth, died of a complication of scurvy and the pox, which he got from a loathsome negro, whom we afterwards gave to the prisoners that she might do no further mischief on board ".[2]

A course of intensive battle training was now entered upon. A sham fight was staged between the two frigates, the *Dutchess* hoisting the Spanish flag ; and the whole engagement was realistic even to such details as covering two men in red lead to act as wounded for the surgeons' practice. These exercises revealed a high standard of operational efficiency, although petty dissension still reigned amongst the officers. Ever since the attack on Guayaquil, when they had first come into open conflict, Dover and Rogers still chose to disagree. During some of the conferences Rogers's views had often been hotly opposed by Dover, who had quite frequently received the support of Captain Courtney. As a result of these quarrels Thomas Dover asked to leave the *Duke*, and transferred himself as Second Captain on board the *Dutchess*. The Committee of officers agreed ; but at Rogers's instigation the following order was passed : " We, the underwritten, appointed part of a Committee now present on board the *Duke* do certify, that Captain Dover requested to go on board the *Dutchess* ; and desired us to take notice it was his own choice so to do."[3]

[1] WOODES ROGERS, *A Cruising Voyage round the World*, 1712. Cassell, 1928, 186.

[2] *Ibid.*, 185.

[3] *Ibid.*, 197.

With Dover and Rogers now separated, dissensions amongst the officers grew less; and the voyage became invigorated with renewed purpose, when it was unanimously decided to attempt the capture of a Spanish treasure ship from Manila.

CHAPTER IX

AN ENGAGEMENT AT SEA

A sail !—a sail—a promised prize to hope !
Her nation—flag—how speaks the telescope ?
She walks the waters like a thing of life,
And seems to dare the elements to strife.
Who would not brave the battle-fire—the wreck,
To move the monarch of her peopled deck ?

BYRON

ALL the romance of privateering in Elizabeth's time centred around the capture of Spanish galleons plying yearly between Manila and Acapulco. This Spanish trade across the Pacific to the Philippines was mentioned by John Chilton, who visited Mexico in 1568. The following year he visited the port of Navidad, sixty-six leagues from Mexico, where " always in the month of April, all the ships that come out of the South Seas lay their merchandise ashore, the most part whereof is mantles made of cotton, wool, wax and platters gilt, made of earth, and much gold ".[1]

It was every seaman's dream to have a share in the plunder of one of these richly laden galleons ; but only one Englishman, Thomas Cavendish, had previously captured a treasure ship one hundred and twenty-two years before. The prize vessel had been taken to Port Seguro, where " we loaded our own two ships with forty tons of the richest merchandise, and burned all the rest, as well she has goods to the quantity of six hundred tons of rich merchandise, because we are unable to bring it away ".[2]

By November, 1709, we find the small British squadron diligently patrolling the Californian coast off Cape St. Lucas,

[1] E. R. BEAZLEY, *Voyages and Travels*, 1903, Vol. I, 268.
[2] *Ibid.*, 288.

the same locality in which Cavendish had encountered the
Spanish ships. It proved to be a tedious vigil, which tested
the temper of the men to the extreme. During the whole of
November there was no sign of the treasure ships ; several of
the men mutinied and were confined in irons ; two others
broke open the ship's stores and stole some of the rapidly
diminishing stock of victuals ; gambling amongst the whole
ship's company had reached such a feverish pitch that it began
to undermine discipline, as many officers and men had
already lost all their share of plunder. A few minor episodes
broke the monotony of their patrol. On board the *Duke* a
baby was born to a coloured girl captured at Guayaquil and
subsequently employed as a laundress. Mr. Wasse, the chief
surgeon, acted as midwife, in which duties he seemed somewhat unpractised.

This morning one of our negro women cried out, and was delivered
of a girl of a tawny colour ; Mr. Wasse, our chief surgeon was forced to
discharge the office of a midwife in a close cabin provided for that purpose ;
but what we most wanted was good liquor to keep up, or initiate, the
women's laudable custom of a refreshing cup on such an occasion. I
accidentally found a bottle of thick, strong, Peru wine, a good part of
which was given to the sick woman, who desired more than we could
spare her. She had not been full six months amongst us so that the child
could belong to none of our company. But to prevent the other she-
negro (called Daphne) from being debauched in our ship I gave her a
strict charge to be modest, with threats of severe punishment if she was
found otherwise. One of the *Dutchess's* black nymphs having transgressed this way, was lately whipped at the capstan. This I mention to
satisfy the censorious that we do not countenance lewdness, and that we
took those women on board, only because they spoke English and begged
to be admitted as laundresses, cooks and seamstresses.[1]

Towards the end of December there was still no sign of
the treasure ship, and as provisions were at low ebb, it was
decided to make for the island of Guam. Hope of intercepting
the Spanish ship had almost been abandoned, when the early
morning look-out on the *Duke* spied a sail to the south, about
seven leagues distant. Immediately the white ensign was
hoisted and both frigates gave chase ; but the sea was calm
and only a slight breeze carried them slowly towards the

---

[1] WOODES ROGERS, *A Cruising Voyage round the World*, 1712. Cassell,
1928, 204.

enemy. By evening both frigates were cleared for action, but night fell before they were within range,

At dawn the Spanish vessel was about a league off the *Duke*'s weather-bow, with the *Dutchess* another league astern, and as all three ships were becalmed, Rogers ordered oars to be put out. Over an hour's strenuous rowing had resulted in only slight progress, when a breeze sprang up which slowly wafted them towards the enemy. To Rogers's dismay, there was no liquor to fortify the spirits of the men (as was the custom prior to an engagement) so he ordered a large kettle of chocolate to be boiled up and distributed instead. Afterwards they all went to prayers ; but ere long their devotions were disturbed by the enemy's gunfire.

The Spanish ship, which the *Duke* now engaged single-handed as the *Dutchess* could not close with her in time, was bristling with cannon, and carried powder bowls at each yard-arm to prevent a boarding party. She presented a most formidable aspect. As the *Duke* slowly approached she came under strong fire from the enemy's stern chasers, to which she was only able to return fire from her less formidable fore-cannon. Relentlessly Rogers held the *Duke* to her course, and eventually ranged her alongside the galleon, whence he gave her several raking broadsides.

The fight was hotly contested, until Rogers, with superb seamanship, manœuvred the *Duke* across the bow of the Spanish ship, and vigorously plied his guns from this almost invulnerable position, as the Spaniards were only able to bring their fore chasers and small-arms fire to bear. The precision and rapidity of the British gunners was apparent from the start of the engagement, and after hotly resisting for an hour and a half the Spanish ship struck her colours, just as the *Dutchess* also opened fire with a volley of cannon and small shot.

The galleon, of 420 tons, commanded by Don John Pichberty, bore the long name of *Nostra Signora de la Incarnacia del Singana* ; she mounted twenty cannon, twenty patereroes, and carried a complement of one hundred and ninety-three men, of whom nine were killed, ten wounded, and several blown up and burnt with powder. On board the *Duke* only two were wounded, Rogers, and an Irish landsman. The commander's wound was serious. The bullet passed through his cheek carrying away part of his teeth and upper jaw ; but he bore the wound with such fortitude that as he lay writhing on the deck, and unable to speak, he continued to deliver his battle orders in writing.

The two ships and their prize made haste to Port Segura in California. Captain Dover transferred to the new prize, now renamed the *Batchelor*, whilst the *Dutchess* and *Marquis* immediately put to sea in search of further quarry. Rogers was under the care of the surgeons, who were most anxious that he should remain in port until his wounds were healed ; but a few days later when an enemy sail was sighted, he could no longer resist the opportunity of assisting his consorts in battle.

As the *Duke* weighed anchor, the other two ships were already engaging the enemy, and she was still twelve miles to leeward, with only a light breeze to aid her progress. Meanwhile the British ships continued to engage the much larger galleon until late afternoon, when the *Marquis*, being temporarily disabled, withdrew from the fight. The damage repaired, she renewed the attack with great vigour for a further two hours, whilst the *Dutchess* (having borne the main brunt of the fighting all day) sailed to windward of the enemy, in order to repair her tattered rigging and leaking hull. As soon as the damage was made good, she once again bore down on the galleon, and fought on until nightfall.

Meanwhile Rogers was crowding on all the sail he could muster, so that by dawn of the second day of the engagement, when the wind had freshened and shifted, he was able to bring the *Duke* within range. The *Dutchess* continued to direct her fire across the Spaniard's bow, so Rogers was unable to bring his vessel across the enemy's stern, for fear of intercepting the cross fire of his consort : instead he ranged his ship alongside the enemy and raked her fore and aft with rapid broadsides for nearly two hours. But Rogers found, as the *Dutchess* and *Marquis* had also experienced, that their largest round shot (six pounders) did very little damage to the galleon's stout hull. The Spanish flag still obstinately fluttered from her mainmast, "all our battering signifying little beyond killing two men in her tops, and shattering her rigging".[1] Their adversary not only withstood this withering fire, but retaliated most effectively by putting a couple of shots into the *Duke*'s mainmast which shattered most of her rigging and temporarily disabled her. Undaunted, Rogers tried to close with the enemy and board her, but a fireball landed on the *Duke*'s quarter-deck, blew up a chest of gun powder, and enveloped the ship in flames. Again Rogers was seriously wounded. "Just before we blew up on the quarter deck", he writes, "I was again unfortunately wounded by a Splinter in the Left Foot, part of my Heel-Bone being struck out, and all under my Ankle cut above half thro', which bled very much before it could be dressed, and weaken'd me so that I could not stand, but lay on my back in great misery."[2] Refusing to be carried below, he continued to direct operations, and to encourage his men from where he lay.

There were now twenty killed and wounded on the *Dutchess*, eleven on the *Duke*, and aboard the *Marquis* two men had been scorched with powder, so that in all three ships only one hundred and twenty fit men remained to form a boarding party. It was evident that the galleon was well equipped to repel such an invasion, as boarding netting stretched fore and aft along the gunwale and extended high into the rigging ; she was also fitted with numerous ' close quarters ' containing powder chests and loopholes for small-arms fire. Repeatedly both frigates tried to get within boarding range, but on each occasion they were beaten off with heavy damage.

The fight had now lasted eight hours, during which time the British ships had received a severe pounding, so they withdrew in order to hold a council of war on board the *Duke*. It was at once decided to break off the engagement, as ammunition was short, and the *Duke*'s mainmast, which was shot through in two places, threatened to fall at any moment.

The galleon, which was the new 900-ton flagship of the Manila fleet, "lay with her mainyard aback, expecting

---

[1] WOODES ROGERS, *A Cruising Voyage round the World*, 1712. Cassell, 1928, 223.

[2] *Ibid.*, 224.

another brush ",[1] but the frigates were content to accompany
her until nightfall. "The fight was o'er; the flashing
through the gloom which robes the cannon as he wings a
tomb, had ceased."

Later, it was discovered that the Spanish ship carried four
hundred and fifty men, mounted sixty brass cannon; and
whilst trying to capture her, the British had ineffectively
fired five hundred cannon balls into her stoutly built hull.

At nightfall the three battered ships made haste to rejoin
their first prize at Port Segura. Here the surgeons, armed
with scalpel and saw, went about their bloody task, striking
more fear than a whole fleet of Spanish galleons, as without
either anæsthetics or antiseptics, they amputated limbs,
dressed burns, and blindly probed for bullets buried deep in
the flesh. On board the *Duke*, Thomas Young, a Welshman,
"lost one of his legs"; another seaman whose "face was
miserably torn", was crudely sutured; John Gold had a
bullet extracted from his thigh; a Portuguese died from
abdominal wounds; and a Spanish pilot, who had been shot
in the throat with a musket ball, "which lodg'd so deep,
the Doctors could not come at it", also died.[2] There were
more gory scenes on board the *Dutchess*; so that :—

> . . . Even and morn
> With their hammocks for coffins, the seamen aghast,
> Like dead men, the dead limbs of their comrades cast
> Down the deep.

Meanwhile the fit men were busily engaged in repairing
the damaged ships; and the drain on their rations was eased
by dispatching the Spanish prisoners (who had given
promissory notes) to Acapulco in a barque. Whilst preparations for the next stage of their voyage to Guam were going
ahead, a serious dispute arose as to the appointment of a
Commander for the *Batchelor*. Captain Dover, having a
large money-stake in the ships, was, much against Rogers's
wish, proposed by the majority of officers for this post.
Rogers states that the other officers were "too willing to

---

[1] WOODES ROGERS, *A Cruising Voyage round the World*, 1712. Cassell,
1928, 222.
[2] *Ibid.*, 224.

complement Capt. Dover with the chief Command of the Prize; which till now I thought he would not have accepted, his Posts already being above a Commander of any of our Prizes; but I and my Officers are against it; because we believe Capt. Frye or others, are fitter Persons to take Charge of her, which we insisted on ".[1]

The dispute became serious, as neither party would give way, with the result that all the officers were divided on this issue into two uncompromising factions. However the majority of them, who still supported Captain Dover, protested against Rogers's obstinacy :—

We held a general Committee on board the *Duke* the 6th Day of January 1709-10 for appointing a Commander and other Officers for the said Prize, call'd by the Spaniards, when in their Possession, *Nostra Signora de la Incarnacia del Singana*, but now named by us the *Batchelor Frigate*, wherein it was carried by Majority of Votes for Capt. Thomas Dover, who came out second Captain of the *Duke*, and President of this Committee, and Owner of a very considerable Part of both Ships, *Duke* and *Dutchess*, to command the said Prize, we thinking him the most proper Person for the Interest of the Owners and Company; we likewise proposing to put two of the best of our Officers on board, to command under him, and manage the navigating Part of the said Ship during the Voyage, with other substantial Officers and Men, sufficient to work the Ship and take Care of her.

Now whereas Capt. Woodes Rogers, Commander of the *Duke*, and several of his Officers, Members of this Committee, did refuse to sign to the agreement of the said Committee (the like never having been refus'd by any before, when carried by Majority of Voices) to acknowledge the said Capt. Thomas Dover Commander of the Ship *Batchelor Frigate*; we do hereby, in the behalf of the Owners of the ships *Duke* and *Dutchess*, our selves and Company, Protest against the unadvis'd Proceedings and Practice of the said Capt. Woodes Rogers, and the rest of the Officers of the Committee, that refus'd to sign and agree to the same, it being directly contrary to the Owners Orders and Instructions (Reference being had thereto) and the Union and Peace of the Ships Companies (by them likewise recommended). And whatever Damage may ensue, either by Loss of Time, Want of Provisions, or Men sufficient to manage the said Ship, or any Mutiny or Disagreement that may arise from hence between the Ships Companies, or any other Disaster whatsoever, &c. we do likewise Protest against, in the behalf of the Owners, ourselves, and Company, as aforesaid; expecting from the said full Satisfaction and Reparation of all

---

[1] WOODES ROGERS, *A Cruising Voyage round the World*, 1712. Cassell, 1928, 223.

Losses and Damages whatsoever, that may happen to the said Ship during her Voyage to Great Britain.[1]

The deadlock lasted another two days; and it is apparent from Rogers's account that Dover was equally obstinate :—

Capts. Courtney and Cooke came to me, where they agreed to a Paper that was drawn up while we were all together, in such a Manner as I thought would have satisfied every one. Capt. Courtney carried this Agreement to Capt. Dover to sign it, not doubting but all would be content with what we had concluded; yet to our Surprize, they spent the Remainder of the Day, and instead of making Capt. Dover comply with it, undid all, and brought a Paper which impower'd him to be Sole Commander, without the least Restraint, of not molesting those that should navigate the Ship, but to order every thing as he should think fit.[2]

At another meeting aboard the *Batchelor*, Rogers suggested that Captain Cooke be appointed Commander, but the latter declined the offer, in order to support Dover's claims. Although still in pain and greatly weakened by his recent wounds, Rogers firmly held his ground, as this forthright note shows :—

My opinion is, That 'tis not for the Safety of the rich Spanish Prize, that Capt. Dover command her, because his Temper is so violent, that capable Men cannot well act under him, and himself is uncapable. Our Owners directed me to use the securest Method to bring the Ship home, if we should have the good Fortune to take her; and 'tis not so, if an ignorant Person have the Command; and tho' it may be pretended that he'll not command the sailing Part, there are other Parts necessary for a Commander; so that whosoever has the Charge of one, ought to act wholly in the rest, or else Confusion follows a mix'd Command, that would be very pernicious in this Case; and which it highly concerns us to beware of. I am content, and desire Capt. Dover may be aboard, and have Power to take Care of the Cargo, and all the Liberty and Freedom in her, he can in reason otherwise desire, and that none may have the like Power on board the Prize but himself. This is my Opinion.

Jan. 9. 1709–10. Woodes Rogers.[3]

From the beginning of the argument Dover was supported by the majority of Senior Officers, and though modifications were later designed to appease Rogers, he was eventually given command of the *Batchelor*. However, Callander,

[1] WOODES ROGERS, *A Cruising Voyage round the World*, 1712. Cassell, 1928, 224–225.
[2] *Ibid.*, 223.
[3] *Ibid.*, 226–227.

commenting on the voyage in 1768, passes the following rather harsh judgement on Dover, which in the light of this particular dispute at least is not wholly justified. " He was a man of rough temper, and could not easily agree with people about him : but his untoward disposition had one good effect, which was this ; that it hindered his making any party to support him in his ill humours."[1]

It was finally agreed that Captain Dover be appointed Commander of the *Batchelor* with Mr. Fry and Mr. Stretton in joint charge of navigating the ship. Although Rogers deplores " our great misfortune to have a paper war amongst ourselves ", yet he cannot forbear to allow the incident to end without a final protest. " It is agreed, by the Majority of this Council, that Capt. Robert Frye and Capt. William Stretton, shall both act in equal Posts in the sole Navigating, Sailing and Ingaging, if Occasion should be, under Capt. Tho. Dover, on board the Batchelor Frigate, and that the said Capt. Tho. Dover shall not molest, hinder or contradict 'em in their Business ; and we do appoint Alexander Selkirk Master."[2]

The *Batchelor* was manned by seamen taken from each of the other ships, together with thirty-six Indians which made up her complement to one hundred and ten men. All was ready by the evening of January 10th, 1710, when the four ships, *Duke*, *Dutchess*, *Marquis*, and *Batchelor*, all heavily laden, left the coast of California for the island of Guam, in the Ladrones group, being the first stage of their long journey home. Provisions were extremely short and strict rationing had to be enforced ; men caught stealing food were severely flogged by their messmates. The offenders were ordered to " the Main Jeers, where every Man of the Watch gave 'em a Blow with a Cat of Nine-tails, and their Messmates being privy to the Theft were put in Irons ".[3]

There were many deaths during the voyage to Guam, some from wounds, and others due to malnutrition, and the heavy

---

[1] JOHN CALLANDER, *Voyages to Terra Australis Cognita*, 1768, Vol. III, 232.
[2] WOODES ROGERS, *A Cruising Voyage round the World*, 1712. Cassell, 1928, 228.
[3] *Ibid.*, 231.

labour of constantly working the pumps. Amongst those who died was a negro called "Deptford", who being much addicted to stealing provisions, was thrown overboard without regrets, as "his Room was more acceptable than his Company at this time".

The long voyage to Guam, a distance of over six thousand miles, occupied two months during which the best day's run was one hundred and sixty-eight miles and the worst forty-one miles. On the whole the voyage was uneventful except for a celebration amongst the officers on Valentine's Day, when they drew up a list of the "fair ladies in Bristol that were any ways related to them, and drank their health in punch, and ' to a happy Sight of 'em all ' ".[1]

As the squadron approached the Island of Guam, which was a Spanish possession, several native proahs came out to greet them. Amongst them were two Spaniards, who viewed the new arrivals with suspicion, and could not be tempted on board, until Rogers hoisted the Spanish flag and assured them that they were friends from New Spain. But as soon as the Spaniards stepped on board the *Duke*, one was detained as a hostage, whilst the other was dispatched to the Governor with the following note :—

Sir,
We being Servants to Her Majesty of Great Britain, and stopping at these Islands in Our Way to the East Indies, will not molest the Settlement, provided you deal friendly by us. We will pay for whatever Provisions and Refreshment you have to spare, in such manner as best agrees with your Conveniency, either in Money, or any Necessaries you want. But if after this civil Request you deny us, and do not act like a Man of Honour, you may immediately expect such Military Treatment, as we are with ease able to give you.[2]

This letter appears to have acted like a charm on the Governor of Guam, as he replied at once with a present of four bullocks, together with plenty of limes, oranges, and coconuts. The British sailors enjoyed their week's stay on the island. They were so astonished at the speed and handiness of the native proahs, which " may run twenty miles

---

[1] WOODES ROGERS, *A Cruising Voyage round the World*, 1712. Cassell, 1928, 247.
[2] *Ibid.*, 264.

an hour for they passed our ships like a bird flying ", that
Rogers bought one intending to try it out on the lake in
St. James's Park, London. Also the ships' officers became very
friendly with the Spanish Governor, who was well entertained
aboard each ship in turn ; and as he had been most civil in
supplying them with all their requirements, they gave him a
farewell present of " two negro boys dress'd in liveries together
with scarlet clothe, serge and six pieces of cambric ".

After leaving Guam they ran into a tropical storm with
thunder, lightning, and occasional water spouts, one of which
almost broke over the *Marquis*, had not the *Dutchess* dispelled
it just before it reached her, by firing two shots.

On May 29th the four ships safely came to anchor at the
island of Bouton in the Moluccas. The quarrel between
Dover and Rogers was still not healed ; at Bouton, Dover,
who had acquired a Malayan interpreter *en route*, refused to
send the man on board the *Duke* to assist Rogers with his
language difficulties. The King of Bouton provided them
with provisions for a further three weeks' voyage to Java
where they anchored in Batavia roads, which was the first
large port they had seen for nearly two years.

After the hardships of their voyage Batavia was a paradise,
where the crew could get drunk on arrack at 8d. a gallon,
and buy sugar for a penny a pound. Several men deserted at
Batavia, and thereby forfeited their hard-earned share of the
prize money ; but this seemed preferable to them than
constant work at the pumps and they were readily replaced
by thirty-four Dutchmen. The hold of the *Batchelor* was
repacked and stored ; all the ships were cleaned and careened,
except the *Marquis*, which was found unfit to proceed to
Europe, and was sold for 575 Dutch dollars. An advance
payment was made to the officers to cover their expenses in
Batavia and it is recorded that Dover headed the list with
2000 pieces of eight, Captains Courtney and Rogers taking
only 400 each.

After a stay of nearly four months in Java, the three ships
sailed from Batavia, bound directly for the Cape of Good
Hope. The *Duke* was still very leaky due to the battering
she had sustained in her last engagement, and throughout the

voyage there was great difficulty in keeping her afloat. Mr. James Wasse, the surgeon, died on the passage to the Cape, and was buried next day, " with our naval ceremonies as usual being a very useful honest man, a good surgeon, and brought up at Leyden in the study of Physick as well as surgery ".[1]

On December 28th, 1710, the three ships arrived at the Cape, and as was the common sequel of a long voyage during those days, sixteen sick men were sent ashore with scurvy. Several days were occupied refitting, and some of the cargo of gold plate had to be sold in order to buy provisions. Their departure from the Cape of Good Hope was deferred until a large number of homeward bound ships were ready to sail in convoy. At daybreak on April 5th, 1711, a combined fleet of twenty armed ships sailed from Table Bay under the command of a Dutch vice-admiral. As soon as they were under way, the British captains (including our physician) were signalled to go on board the flagship to receive their sailing orders, " which were very particular and obligatory punctually observ'd ".[2]

During the last phase of the voyage, Dover's ship, the *Batchelor*, was so slow that she could not keep pace with the convoy, and frequently had to be towed ; but otherwise he handled the vessel quite capably. After crossing the line for the eighth time, the convoy steered a course to the westward of the Azores, and then north-westward around the Shetlands. This wide detour was made for fear of meeting French warships. As the fleet sailed into northern waters the ships were enveloped in a thick fog for several days, during which the flagship kept them together by firing two shots every half hour, which was answered by a single shot from the other vessels.

At last on July 23rd, 1711, the fleet safely came to anchor in Texel roads, Holland, after a voyage of nearly four years, in which Captain Thomas Dover, the truculent bachelor of physic, had played a leading, and at times, militant role.

---

[1] WOODES ROGERS, *A Cruising Voyage round the World*, 1712. Cassell, 1928, 300.

[2] *Ibid.*, 302.

CHAPTER X

THE FINANCIAL AFTERMATH

He that is rich and wants to fool away
A good round sum in North America
Let him subscribe himself a headlong sharer
And Asses' ears shall honour him as bearer.

ANON.

THE voyage, as far as Holland, had been eminently successful. The expedition had amply demonstrated the supremacy of British seamanship; it had acquitted itself well in battle with the Spaniards; and now within a few days from home, each man was eagerly awaiting his share of plunder, as personal gain rather than prestige had always been the expedition's aim. But although their long voyage had almost ended, many unaccustomed hazards lay ahead; financial intrigues, and the tedious procedure of the law courts were to vex the patience of these sturdy adventurers. Ever since their arrival in Eastern waters, agents of the powerful East India Company had been carefully watching the activities of the Bristol privateers, as the directors of that company were collecting evidence against them, for what they alleged was an infringement on their trading monopoly. As soon as the Bristol privateers reached Holland, twelve East India Company agents were sent there in order to report any sale of cargo from the British ships.

Recently the East India Company had entered upon an important phase in its long history, as two years before the return of the Bristol ships, the 'old' and 'new' companies had merged to form the powerful "United Company of Merchants of England Trading to the East Indies".[1] The

---

[1] A. D. INNES, *Maritime and Colonial Expansion of England 1603–1714*, 360.

influence of this company extended to every city in the
kingdom and affected directly or indirectly almost every great
mercantile fortune.   Although there were many independent
merchants anxious to trade in the East, they were debarred
from so doing except under special licence which could only
be obtained from the monopolist company.   To further their
interests the East India Company had entered the political
arena ;   and often by sheer corruption they had wrested
boroughs from the Tory landlords who had for generations
controlled them.   " The mischievous consequence ", wrote
Bolingbroke, " which had been foreseen and foretold too at
the establishment of these Corporations, appeared visibly.
The country gentlemen were vexed, put to great expenses,
and even baffled by them at their elections ;   and amongst the
members of every Parliament numbers were immediately or
indirectly under their influence."[1]

In 1711 the Tory Government led by Robert Harley, Earl
of Oxford, was making searching enquiries into the large sums
of money which the East India Company had expended
amongst its parliamentary nominees, who wielded their
influence in the Whig cause.   But no active measures were
taken to suppress these intrigues, as Harley was then busily
engaged in launching a similar, though more grandiose
venture.   This was the South Sea Company formed by a
group of merchants, and sponsored by the government with
the object of restoring public credit, following the losses
incurred by continental wars and the dismissal of the Whig
ministry.   These merchants took upon themselves the national
debt of £10,000,000, in return for which the government
promised them, for a certain period, an interest of six per cent.
In this respect the South Sea Company was virtually the
government banker, or at any rate, in competition with the
Bank of England for this privilege.   But a more grandiose
aspect of this enterprise was its trading monopoly for the
Eastern seaboard of South America whence it had visionary
ideas of untold wealth from the inexhaustible gold and silver
mines of Mexico and Peru.

---

[1] W. E. H. LECKY, *England in the 18th Century*, Vol. I, 199.

Such, briefly, were the financial affairs of state, when the
Bristol owners, having heard of the intentions of the East
India Company, petitioned the Attorney General and the
Earl of Oxford to intervene on their behalf. The owners
respectfully submitted that their ships had never contravened
their Letters of Marque, nor had they traded (other than to
provide themselves with necessities) during the voyage. But
although they received the support of Harley, and the
Attorney General, who expressed the wish that the differences
" might be accomodated ",[1] the Directors of the East India
Company decided to refer the matter to their Committee of
Law Suits. Two days later, another letter from the Attorney
General on behalf of the Bristol owners was read at a meeting
of the company. It stated that the Bristol privateers were
" without any the least part of goods for Traffique or
Commerce " ;[2] that their captains held commissions from the
Lord High Admiral; and that the prize goods, though of
European manufacture, had all been captured from Spanish
ships in the South Seas. The return voyage via the Indies
(through the waters over which the Company held exclusive
rights) had been necessary owing to the poor condition of
their vessels which could hardly have withstood the gales
off Cape Horn. The letter ended by stating that should the
Company persist in their intention of appropriating the ships,
then the owners' only recourse would be to sell their plunder
in foreign markets. But the Directors were not in a conciliatory mood, for they desired the Attorney General to notify
the Bristol owners that their explanation was " not to their
satisfaction ".[3]

Meanwhile there was much activity in Holland. Representatives of the Bristol merchants went there to discuss
matters with their commanders. Lord Drummond, an agent
of the Earl of Oxford, also visited Holland, from where he
expressed a favourable opinion of Thomas Dover's ability as

---

[1] *Minutes of the Court of Directors of the East India Company,* July 25,
1711, Public Records Office.

[2] *Ibid.,* July 27, 1711.

[3] *Ibid.*

a negotiator in a report to his patron. " Our Admiralty ", he says, " promises eight men-of-war to convoy over the English East India ships if they can be ready, but the Bristol South Seas men are frightened by your East India Company's threatenings, and will in all probability stay and sell their cargo here. Dampier is alive, and one Captain Dover alias Doctor Dover seems to be the man of sense and conduct in all that affair."[1]

Captain Dover played a large part in the negotiations in Holland. Along with Hollidge, a representative of the Bristol owners, he prepared a detailed list of all the places visited during the voyage, together with an account of the goods they had sold there. This document having been signed and sworn to be true before an advocate, was dispatched to the East India Company. In hopes of a share in the profits, one Stephen Creagh also hastened to Holland, where he induced two hundred and nine members of the crew to sign a paper appointing him their agent for five per cent commission. Later, Creagh was the instigator of much litigation, which protracted the final settlement.

On August 1st, 1711, the directors of the East India Company finally resolved, in spite of all protests, " that the Court will seize the two privateers of Bristol, called the ' Duke ' and ' Dutchess ', and their prize called the ' Batchelor ' together with their cargoes ".[2] A few weeks later their Dutch agents were told " to have an eye upon the Proceedings of the ' Duke ' and ' Dutchess ' Bristol Privateers, and their prize and give them an account thereof, particular if they unlode all or any Part of their respective Cargoes or other goods or Treasure ".[3]

Whilst Texel was seething with intrigue, the Bristol owners were still trying to reach a settlement in London. Three of their number asked to discuss the matter with the company, when they hoped to show their innocence. But

---

[1] *Harley Papers*, Letter from J. Drummond to Earl of Oxford, Vol. XXXIV, ff. 192a.

[2] *Minutes of the Court of Directors of the East India Company*, August 17th, 1711.

[3] *East India Company Miscellanies*, 1710–13, Vol. III, 125.

the East India Company directors refused their request, and somewhat pompously added, " That since you insist on your innocence, for then the Law will be on your side, tho' the Court have reason to differ in Opinion ; but if you will lay any proposals before the Court in writing, they will give a speedy answer in writing, and are very inclinable to do anything that is reasonable, in order to bring the Riches aboard these ships to England. And no advantage shall be taken on either side. But in case no agreement be made all papers to be destroyed."[1]

The owners were not impressed by this formal proposal, whereupon they informed the Company that " we have nothing further to offer ".[2] Yet in spite of the rebuff, the Bristol merchants had decided to risk allowing their ships to sail for England, and in company with East Indiamen, the privateers reached the Thames estuary on October 1st, 1711. That they had " gotten to the Downs " was duly reported by Spencer, an agent of the East India Company, whereupon the directors sent three men to assist him in capturing the ships as soon as they reached London.[3] The actual seizure of the ships when they anchored at Erith twelve days later was a farcical anticlimax to their long and hazardous voyage. The agents were instructed to deliver the following note to the commander of each ship : " We seize this ship and all goods aboard for the use and on behalf of the United Company of Merchants of England to the East Indies."[4] As they were prevented from going aboard they had to be content with throwing their acquisition notes on the deck of each ship. In spite of their assertive attitude, the directors did not confirm their claims in court, but instead tentatively applied to Doctors' Commons for an opinion, whence it was learned that legal action would be unwise.

The Bristol owners were still in a conciliatory mood, and again sent three of their representatives to treat with the

---

[1,2] *Minutes of the Court of Directors of the East India Company*, August 17, 1711.

[3] *Ibid.*, October 3, 1711.

[4] *Ibid.*, October 12, 1711.

directors; this time a meeting took place, and on March
21st, 1712, a settlement was reached. The owners of the
privateers agreed to pay £6000 together with a bribe of
£161 (paid to an unnamed agent of the company) and thereafter the East India Company promised to forgo any further
claims. This easy success encouraged the Company of Silk
Throwers and Throwsters to bring another claim against the
privateers under an Act of William III, which prohibited the
introduction of silk from the East Indies, except under a duty
of fifteen per cent. However, this company received no
payment, as the Bristol merchants were able to prove that
all their silk goods had been made in Spain.

During these disputes unloading and warehousing of prize
goods was going on at Leadenhall; and the *Batchelor* was
formally condemned as a prize in the High Court of Admiralty.
But Creagh suddenly put a stop to further proceedings after
a quarrel with Captain Rogers. The latter distrusted him
and advised the other members of the crew not to employ him
as their agent. Whereupon Creagh charged Rogers with
" fraud against the owners ".[1] The case came before the
Lord Chancellor, where it was soon obvious that Creagh was
a rogue and a trickster. One of the witnesses well acquainted
with Creagh stated that " he knows nothing good of him ".[2]
The lawsuit dragged on interminably. Creagh kept his own
interests to the forefront, and even refused to allow members
of the crew to give evidence against their commanders, who
were alleged to have secretly sold a considerable quantity of
plunder. Although Creagh's action was dismissed, he
continued to hold up the proceedings by charging Captain
Freake, one of the owners, with fraud; and later interfered
with the warehousing of goods, so that even the men he
purported to represent came to distrust him, to the extent
of suggesting that he was acting in the owner's interest.

After a year's litigation, the Lord Chancellor ruled that
the prize goods must be sold as soon as possible and the
profits were to be divided in the ratio of one-third to the

---

[1] *Creagh* v. *Rogers and Others, Entry Book, Chancery Decrees and Orders,*
1712–13, C. 33/319, H. 26, Public Records Office.
[2] *Ibid.*, H. 414, 415.

crew and two-thirds to the owners. With regard to Creagh's claims the Chancellor ruled that only the men who had signed a document appointing him their agent were required to pay his commission. A few goods were sold privately, but the majority were publicly auctioned, and realized a total of £147,975 12s. 4d. Thus, according to the Chancellor's ruling the two-thirds due to the owners should have amounted to £98,650; but bribes, lawsuits, cross suits, and incidental charges whittled down the owners' profit to £50,109. They were dissatisfied with their small gain and immediately appealed against this decision.

The owners claimed that the award to the crew of " storm money " for the capture of Guayaquil be disallowed, as they contended that the city had been " abandoned by the enemy ". However the Master rejected their appeal on the grounds that both Captains Dover and Courtney (who were also owners) had stated that the city had in fact been stormed. Another appeal which was also rejected was the owners' contention that the money paid to the East India Company should be shared by them and the crew alike.

During these long proceedings the owners, most of whom resided in Bristol, had appointed six of their number (including Dover) to look after their interests in London. These gentlemen proceeded to enjoy themselves at the expense of their Bristol colleagues, and their extravagance impelled Thomas Goldney, the largest shareholder, to protest. He states that the £6000 they paid to the East India Company " was weakly parted with ", as well as a further £161 " for soliciting them to accept it ". The letter ends with a list of items totalling £10,000 which Goldney considered unnecessary expenses. His letter reflects the business methods of the times as it includes such items as " bribes to Custom House Officers " and further large amounts for " tavern expenses and treats ".[1]

Three years after their return the crew had not been paid. Many of the humbler members were reduced to poverty, and even Captain Rogers was declared bankrupt. On June 17th, 1714, thirty-three seamen petitioned the House of Lords.

---

[1] *Chancery Master's Exhibits*, C. 104/160–1, Public Records Office.

The petitioners accused their commanders of defrauding the customs by selling prize goods abroad. They also accused Creagh, "who pretends to act on petitioners' behalf, but commenced the suit without their knowledge ", of deliberately prolonging the proceedings of the Chancery Court. But the Lords refused to intervene on their behalf as matters were still *sub judice* in the High Court of Chancery.

Another year passed, and still the crew had not been paid. On August 31st, 1715, their second protest, *The Humble Petition of the Poor South-Sea Sailors*,[1] was read before the House of Lords. It begins : " Some merchants in Bristol, of whom Captain Thomas Dover, and Captain Stephen Courtney were two " ; and goes on to accuse the chief officers and owners of fraud. They alleged that their commanders had destroyed the " Bills of Lading " of several prizes, and thereby withheld the true value from the petitioners. Later these captains were alleged to have transferred "divers Chests of Plate (of many Hundred Weight a Piece) out of the *Duke* and *Dutchess* to East Indiamen at Batavia " ;[2] similar embezzlements were said to have taken place at Texel, and again on arrival in England.

The chief officers were also accused of " Cowardise or Corruption" ; as by delaying the attack on Guayaquil for three or four days, they had forfeited much treasure. The petitioners had a grossly exaggerated idea of the total value of the prize goods, as they estimated that even after their officers had embezzled nearly £2,000,000 worth of goods abroad, the cargo unloaded in London was worth £1,000,000. Their Lordships dismissed the petition : thus due to the interminable lawsuits, claims, cross-suits, and appeals it was not until five years after the voyage that all the crew were finally paid. Their bounty depended on whether they had originally signed on for " half purchase, half pay ", which was more usual than " full purchase, no pay " : but in either case few of them received more than fifty pounds for a voyage which had lasted over three years, and during which nearly one hundred men had lost their lives.

---

[1] *The Humble Petition of the Poor South-Sea Sailors*, August 31, 1715. House of Lords Library.
[2] *Ibid.*

When the profits were finally distributed Dover and Courtney were fortunate, as both being owners as well as members of the crew, they were only slightly influenced by the decision of the Master in Chancery. As the second largest shareholder Thomas Dover originally invested £3312 in the expedition from which he eventually received £6067. Also as a member of the crew he was paid £423 as " physician to the voyage ", £100 " storm money " for his part in the capture of Guayaquil, £24 " plunder money ", and £75 as commander of the *Batchelor*.[1] Therefore he received a total of £6689, more than twice his initial outlay which, together with his family property at Barton, rendered him financially independent, with no need to practise medicine for a livelihood.

The aftermath of the voyage with its prolonged intrigues and corruption had fostered bitterness and distrust amongst all parties. The owners were split with dissension ; the commanders, particularly Rogers and Dover, constantly conflicted ; and whilst the unpaid crew grew more suspicious of everyone, the various agents constantly litigated, largely to their own advantage.

After his return to England it was necessary for Thomas Dover to remain in London for some time in order to safeguard his own financial interests. As one of the owners' representatives he had played a prominent part in all the various negotiations. Also he was responsible for the interests of his sister, the widow of Samuel Hopkins, apothecary to the expedition. Therefore, for four or five years after his return to England, Thomas Dover was fully occupied with his financial affairs in London, occasional visits to his family in Bristol, and to his lands at Barton. Once his affairs were in order, he again began to practise medicine, and about this time he treated one of the royal gardeners for dropsy. But his small practice was probably largely confined to friends and acquaintances, and was more in the nature of a hobby than a serious occupation, as at this time he was not a licentiate

---

[1] B. M. H. ROGERS, " Woodes Rogers Privateering Voyage of 1708–11," *Mariners Mirror*, 1933, **14**, 208.

of the College of Physicians, and therefore not entitled to practise in London.

The exploits of the voyage had aroused considerable public interest, and the subsequent legal disputes gave rise to many exaggerated rumours. Narratives of the voyage by Captains Rogers and Cooke were published in 1712 (the latter's account being dedicated to Robert Harley, Earl of Oxford), and were widely read by a public only too eager to be reassured of the vast wealth of the South Seas. It was a time of great financial speculation when South Sea stock, though occasionally subject to strange and violent fluctuations, was still booming. The success of the Bristol privateers had played a conspicuous part, if not in the actual foundation of the company, certainly in its subsequent chequered and unprosperous career, and served as a further stimulus to public speculation. Callander, after describing the privateering voyage and praising its motives, strongly hints at its relationship with the South Sea Company. "I might, perhaps, go too far", he says, "should I assert that this voyage gave rise to the South Sea Company; but this much I can safely say, that the success of this voyage was what the patrons of that company chiefly insisted upon in their defence, when the plan of it was attacked as insufficient and chimerical."[1]

It is almost certain that the directors of the South Sea Company sought advice on the prospects of their project from the recent experience gained by the Bristol privateers. Also it is most likely that Dr. Dover, who had been recommended to Harley as a "man of sense and conduct",[2] would be one of the officers whose opinion was sought. Thomas Dover certainly had great faith in the South Sea Company, for into that unprosperous venture he now invested the bulk of his hard-earned fortune.

Naval historians were also impressed by the voyage of the Bristol privateers. Captain Berkeley, in his *Naval History of Britain*, also mentioned their exploits. "We have read in very pompous language", he says, "the names of those who

[1] JOHN CALLANDER, *Terra Australis Cognita*, 1768, Vol. III, 379.
[2] *Harley Papers*, Letter from J. Drummond to Earl of Oxford, Vol. XXXIV, ff. 192a.

PLATE V

The track of the *Duke* and *Dutchess* round the world.
Frontispiece to 1st edition of Woodes Rogers's book.

PLATE VI

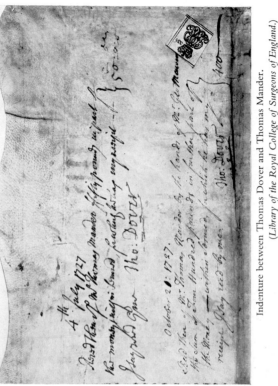

Indenture between Thomas Dover and Thomas Mander.

(Library of the Royal College of Surgeons of England.)

Letter from Thomas Dover to Sir Hans Sloane, April, 1721.

with Great Ships and Great Preparations encompassed the Globe. At this time came in two Privateers of Bristol, who with no more than the common Strength of such vessels, undertook the voyage, and at the end of three years and two months returned."[1]

Alexander Selkirk's life on the uninhabited island of Juan Fernandez thrilled the eighteenth-century public, and in response to their demands more details of his lonely sojourn were included in later narratives of the voyage. Sir Richard Steele, who had met Selkirk on his return to England, recounted his adventures in a leading article in *The Englishman* which reached a wide public ; and finally Defoe swelled the Selkirk story into the immortal romance of *Robinson Crusoe*.

Thus in many ways was public interest kindled in the exploits of the Bristol privateers ; as a narrative of adventure ; as a technical feat of seamanship ; but above all, it provided a further stimulus to the feverish and unparalleled speculations of the early eighteenth-century public : for this expedition was to become the only concrete example of the riches of the South Seas.

At this time Dr. Dover swept smoothly along the flood-tide of success. He was wealthy ; South Sea stock was rising ; and he practised medicine as a hobby. In the coffee-houses he frequented his swashbuckling exploits had assumed a legendary splendour, and he was now moving in a more fashionable milieu. In a letter to her aunt, the Countess of Oxford, Viscountess Dupplin refers to Dr. Dover as " this famous man ".[2] Thus some measure of fame, together with his growing acquaintances amongst people of rank and fortune, influenced his decision to practise henceforth as a London physician.

---

[1] CAPT. GEORGE BERKELEY, *The Naval History of Britain*, 1758, Ch. LXXIV, 684.

[2] *Harley Papers*, Letter from Viscountess Dupplin to Abigail Harley, March 4th, 1720, Vol. XXXIV, ff. 192a, 192b.

CHAPTER XI

PHYSICK IN THE GRAND MANNER

When Radcliffe fell, afflicted Physic cried
How vain my power ! and languished at his side.
When Freind expired, deep-struck, her hair she tore
And speechless fainted, and revived no more
Her flowing grief no further could extend ;
She mourns for Radcliffe, but she dies with Freind.

SAMUEL WESLEY

APART from brief periods in Bristol, Gloucestershire, and a
journey abroad, Thomas Dover practised medicine in London
from about 1716 until just before his death in 1742. But to
recount the bare details of these twenty years or more, during
which our physician strutted across the London medical
arena, would present an inadequate prelude to his interpreta-
tion. It is first necessary to drop the backcloth of the early
eighteenth-century medical scene, and against this background,
focus brief attention on the activities of his contemporaries.

Professor Trevelyan has called the first forty years of the
eighteenth century " an age of transition ",[1] which bridges
the passionate affairs of the Stuarts with the firmer establishment of the Hanoverian dynasty. It was a period of social
instability. There was a contempt for law and order ;
highwaymen, hanged for their crimes, were first acclaimed
as heroes, and the public procession to the gallows became
a triumphal march. Coarseness and brutality tended
to mar the robust spirit of the age. Though caricatures,
Hogarth's paintings of " Gin Alley " and " The Rake's
Progress ", with their canvases crowded with coxcombs,
hussies, harpies, beaux, and bloods, nevertheless faithfully

---

[1] G. M. TREVELYAN, *English Social History*, 1944, 339.

depicted many aspects of public morals. In the coffee-houses fortune hunters, adventurers, and charlatans rubbed shoulders with the learned and the great. Social barriers were loosened. It was a mercenary age. Gambling was rife ; and the national urge for rapid and effortless gain reached fabulous proportions in the misfortunes of the innumerable " bubble " concerns which followed in the wake of the South Sea Company.

Medicine was also passing through one of its less creditable epochs, as physicians were acutely susceptible to the temper of their day. Of all the professions, the reproach of avarice is not proverbially joined to that of medicine, but during the early part of the eighteenth century such a criticism was well justified. Though there were many impoverished physicians, yet at no other period in the history of medicine did leading physicians, as were Sloane, Radcliffe, and Mead, accumulate such vast wealth. Dr. Creighton regards the cynical and mercenary spirit of medical men during the small-pox epidemics of 1710 and 1714 as being " merely the spirit of the time in London ".[1] Even more than in Chaucer's day epidemics of infectious fevers were the physician's largest source of income, and he :—

> Kepte that he wan in pestilence,
> For gold in phisik is a cordial ;
> Therefore he lovede gold in special.

Both Radcliffe and Mead charged their apothecaries who waited on them at the coffee-houses half a guinea for prescriptions written without seeing the patient. One guinea was generally charged for a nearby visit ; but Radcliffe's fee for a consultation at Bow when he was living in Bloomsbury Square was five guineas, so that on his death he was able to leave endowments of over £100,000 (all of which had been derived from medical practice) to Oxford University. Lucrative practice led to the physician's increased social prestige, and many of them adorned themselves with all the trappings of pomp and display. Literature and art frequently depicted the elegantly attired and perfumed physician setting out in his carriage for the favourite coffee-house. His dress

---

[1] C. CREIGHTON, *A History of Epidemics in England*, 1891, Vol. II, 138.

and demeanour, according to a contemporary squib, followed
a strict pattern :—

> Each son of Sol, to make him look more big,
> Had on a large, grave, decent, three tailed wig ;
> His clothes full trimmed, with button holes behind,
> Stiff were the skirts, with buckram stoutly lined,
> The cloth cut velvet, or more revered black,
> Full made, and powder's half way down his back,
> Large decent cuffs, which near the ground did reach,
> With half a dozen buttons fixed on each.
> Grave were their faces—fixed in solemn stare.
> These men struck awe ; their children carried weight,
> In reverend wigs old heads young shoulders bore,
> And twenty-five or thirty seemed three score.

The doctor's equipage was also a matter of great importance ;
whether he visited his patients in a coach drawn by two, four,
or six horses, seemed to indicate the size and importance of
his practice. Though learned men, well versed in the social
graces, many of these early eighteenth-century physicians
tended to be pompous in manner, often unnecessarily abstruse
in speech, grandiloquent, and somewhat histrionic in bearing.
In order to establish themselves in practice, physicians
endeavoured to attract the notice of the public. They did
so in many ways ; some by flaunting their wealth to best
advantage ; others by success in other spheres ; by their
eccentricities, their political influence, or extravagances, they
tried to insinuate themselves into popular favour. The fame
of such physicians now rests on their outstanding success in
practice, or their additions to other fields of knowledge,
rather than upon their contributions to clinical medicine.

The great upward surge of medicine during the preceding
century, led by such giants as Sydenham and Harvey, had lost
its momentum in this era of the ' social ' physician. Dr.
Singer explains this poverty of research during the early
part of the eighteenth century as being due to a desire to
" introduce unitary conceptions into the mass of accumulated
material " from the past. Hence the first half of the eighteenth century " exhibits something of a gap " in the
evolution of biological science.[1]   With a poverty of research in

---

[1] CHARLES SINGER, *A Short History of Medicine*, 1928, 139.

the basic sciences, clinical medicine in England also languished in the doldrums, though not on the Continent. The logical successor of Thomas Sydenham was not an English physician, but Hermann Boerhaave (1668–1738) of Leyden, whose outstanding contribution was the correlation of symptoms with the pathological lesions whence they arose. British pupils flocked to his clinical lectures, and his influence, exerted through his pupils, later led to the fame of the Edinburgh medical school as a great teaching centre. But in London the majority of leading physicians had other interests, which tended to hinder the progress of clinical medicine.

Sydenham's works were now held in high esteem, but only by a section of the profession. Dr. Radcliffe followed his treatment in many ailments. He owed much of his initial success in practice to the use of Sydenham's cooling method in small-pox, and he was, like Sydenham, a liberal advocate of opiates. But on the whole this later generation of physicians seemed well content to follow some of Sydenham's treatment, rather than endeavour to extend the furrows he had ploughed in the wastelands of clinical diagnosis and the natural history of diseases.

Indeed, Sir D'Arcy Power forthrightly condemns the whole period. " The accession of the House of Hanover to the English throne ", he says, " marks the lowest depths to which modern medicine has descended as a scientific pursuit."[1]

The teaching of anatomy and surgery was also greatly hampered by the monopoly granted to the Company of Barber-Surgeons. In 1714, Mr. Cheselden, surgeon to St. Thomas's Hospital, was summoned before the Company, " as he did frequently procure the Dead Bodies of Malefactors from the place of execution, and did dissect the same at his own house ". He promised amendment, " and was excused what had passed with a reproof for the same by the Master at the desire of the Court ".[2]

Though the material condition of the people had improved, their habits were gross. Greater wealth was followed by

---

[1] SIR D'ARCY POWER, *Social England*, 1895, Vol. V, 65. Ed. Traill and Man.

[2] *Ibid.*, 69.

greater self indulgence, and an increased liability to disease. Drunkenness was rife, and in 1726 Dr. Freind made representation on that subject to the House of Commons. Six gallons of spirits per head of the population per annum was an estimate for this period, as against one gallon during the earlier part of this century. The poorer classes in the metropolis endured a deplorably low state of sanitation. They lived in overcrowded houses ; drank from surface wells ; and threw their garbage into the streets, whence it was carried away by the rain in wet weather, or remained to putrefy during the summer. It is, therefore, not surprising to find that malnutrition was common, and epidemics were frequent.

Preventable diseases caused the highest mortality. The plague had disappeared, but epidemics of such fevers as small-pox, typhoid, typhus, relapsing fever, and the ague caused such havoc in the metropolis that the population was only maintained by a constant flow of people from country districts. The mortality from small-pox had greatly increased since the Restoration, until it reached a peak early in the eighteenth century. Epidemics swept through the country with volcanic fury, killing many, disfiguring others, and striking dread into the hearts of the whole populace. There were particularly severe outbreaks in 1710 and 1714, and in 1719 out of a total of 28,347 deaths in London from all causes, small-pox accounted for 3229.

It appears to have been mainly a disease of the upper class, whereas typhus and other fevers took a heavy toll amongst the poor. The mortality from small-pox amongst people of rank and fortune is reflected in a letter of 1720 written by the Duchess of Argyll to the Countess of Bute. After congratulating her on the addition of a daughter to her family of five sons, Her Grace adds, " He that has had the smallpox is as good as two, so mortal as that distemper has been this year in town was never known."[1] Small-pox was regarded as inevitable ; and the most favourable age to acquire

---

[1] SIR D'ARCY POWER, *Johnson's England*, 1933, Vol. II, 281. Ed. Turberville.

it was between five and twenty years, so that in some families when one child had contracted the disease others in the house were also allowed to become infected. There were also occasional epidemics of measles, but scarlet fever was rare, and usually quite mild.

Though on the whole medical science was languishing during the early part of the eighteenth century, there were two notable achievements. In 1719 Westminster Hospital was founded as a dispensary for the treatment of the sick-poor, and in 1725 Guy's Hospital was erected for the care of incurables. The other major achievement was the introduction of inoculation. In 1714 Dr. Emanuel Timon sent an account of "the procuring of the small-pox by incision or inoculation, as it has for sometime been practised at Constantinople",[1] to Dr. Woodward (Gresham Professor of Physic), who read the paper before the Royal Society. Inoculation, having been brought to Constantinople by the Circassians, had been successfully practised in Turkey for forty years, when Lady Mary Wortley Montague, wife of the British Ambassador, realized its merits, and subsequently introduced the method into England on a practical basis. She describes the Turkish method of inoculation in the following letter from Adrianople :—

The smallpox, so fatal and so general among us, is here entirely harmless by the invention of *engrafting*, which is the term they give it. There is a set of old women who make it their business to perform the operation every autumn, in the month of September, when the heat is abated. People send to one another to know if any of their family has a mind to have the smallpox. They make parties for this purpose; and when they are met (commonly fifteen or sixteen together) the old woman comes with a nut shell full of the matter of the best sort of smallpox, and asks what vein you please to have opened. She immediately rips open that you offer to her with a large needle (which gives you no more pain than a common scratch) and puts into the vein as much matter as can lie upon the head of the needle, and after that binds up the little wound with a hollow bit of shell, and in this manner opens four or five veins. The children are in perfect health till the eighth. Then the fever begins to seize them, and they keep their beds two days—very seldom three. . . . I am patriot enough to take pains to bring this useful invention into

---

[1] Sir D'Arcy Power, *Social England*, 1895, Vol. V, 170. Ed. Traill and Man.

fashion in England ; and I should not fail to write to some of our doctors very particularly about it, if I knew any one of them that had virtue enough to destroy such a considerable branch of their revenue for the good of mankind. But that distemper is too beneficial to them not to expose to all their resentment the hardy weight that should undertake to put an end to it.[1]

Lady Montague had her five-year-old son successfully inoculated, and on her return to England persuaded the Prince of Wales to allow the experiment of inoculation to be carried out on seven condemned criminals at Newgate. All the felons had the disease favourably, including one inoculated by the Chinese method at the suggestion of Dr. Mead, who introduced into her nostrils a tent of pus taken from a ripe pustule. The success of this experiment led to the inoculation of the young princesses, Amelia and Caroline, who both had favourable results. Royal favour considerably helped to popularize inoculation, and amongst its earlier advocates was Dr. Thomas Dover :—

I would have cold bathing grow as universal, as I hope inoculation in a short time will do. I should think it unpardonable if I should take no notice of Her Majesty as a great promoter and encourager of this practice. I believe the world will readily allow me, that Her Majesty is as much superior in her understanding of the generality of her sex, as she is superior to them in that station in which Providence so happily for mankind has placed her. How many are those who are ready to run into any mode of fashion, though never so extravagant, if it has but the sanction of the Great! Let Such, on this occasion imitate their Queen. Is it possible they can be solicitous in matters of a trifling nature, and show little or no regard to what is of infinite importance to Mankind? . . . I therefore lament the small and inconsiderable progress which Inoculation has yet made in Great Britain.[2]

But many people, including Defoe, were opposed to this practice. In a long newspaper article printed in 1722 Defoe states what was then a popular prejudice against inoculation. "It is disputed by many," he says, "how far this is consistent with the Divine Laws, and whether it does not come into the Number of Things, which are forbidden by that command, Thou shalt not tempt the Lord thy God."[3] As a footnote he

---

[1] *Chambers Papers for the People*, 1851, Vol. I, VIII, 13.

[2] THOMAS DOVER, *The Ancient Physician's Legacy*, 1742, 6th ed., 94.

[3] DANIEL DEFOE, *Against Inoculation with Smallpox. The Original Weekly Journal and Saturday's Post*, April 28th, 1722.

adds that although the royal children were successfully inoculated, " members of several noble families died of the disease . . . and I must confess I cannot recommend it to practice, upon any Principle ".   Thus in spite of its favourable introduction into England there was much national prejudice against inoculation, which did not come into general use until twenty years later.

Metropolitan practice in Dover's time is well reflected in the lives of his contemporary physicians.   Most of them were versatile men, many of whom attained distinction as poets, wits, antiquarians, and writers.   Dr. John Radcliffe (1650– 1714) reigned supreme when Thomas Dover first began to practise in London.   Radcliffe was no great scholar, and his remarkable success as a physician has been largely attributed to his sound judgement and the common-sense methods he employed.   He owed much to Sydenham, as can be gleaned from his collected prescriptions published two years after his death.   The introduction to this volume suggests that Radcliffe's success was largely due to his reputation as " a quick Discoverer of the Causes of Distempers ".[1]   But with professional pre-eminence Radcliffe seems to have developed an overbearing insolence, which led to the loss of royal favour, though not of royal confidence.   He made no contribution to medical literature, but apart from his six years as a Member of Parliament, he seems to have devoted most of his time to clinical work.   Radcliffe's fame now rests largely on his Oxford benefactions, although Pope was sceptical as to the usefulness of his travelling fellowships :—

> Ev'n Radcliff 's Doctors travel First to France,
> Nor dare to practise till they've learned to dance.

But Thomas Dover had a great respect for Radcliffe, and after praising his travelling fellowships, added with characteristic conceit, " If travelling be necessary to make an accomplished physician, I am very sure that I have travelled more than all the physicians in Great Britain put together ".[2]

---

[1] *Pharmacopœia Radcliffeana*, 1716, 2nd ed., 1.
[2] THOMAS DOVER, *The Ancient Physician's Legacy*, 1742, 6th ed., 7.

Radcliffe's protégé and successor, Richard Mead (1673–
1754), was (after a continental education) elected at the age of
thirty-two as physician to St. Thomas's Hospital. He
attended Queen Anne during her last illness, and later became
physician-in-ordinary to George II. For almost half a
century Dr. Mead was at the head of his profession, which
brought him between £5000 and £6000 a year. He lived
in Great Ormond Street, where his residence became the
repository of all that was curious in nature or in art : for
Dr. Mead was the Mæcenas of his day. There were marble
statues, Etruscan vases, rare manuscripts, intaglios, and
precious coins ; and it was of Mead that Dr. Johnson said,
" he lived more in the broad sunshine of life than almost any
man ".[1]

Mead's best known medical work was a *Discourse concerning
Pestilential Contagion*, published in 1720. During the previous
year the plague had raged in Marseilles and in order to
prevent further spread to Britain, Mead advocated quarantine
measures at all the ports. It was then customary to close the
houses of people stricken with the plague, and to paint a
large red cross on the door, over which was inscribed, " Lord
have Mercy upon us ".[2] But Mead disagreed with this
practice, partly on humanitarian grounds, and also because
the infection was thereby localized within, instead of being
allowed to be dispersed by the wind. Although he had the
most remunerative practice in London, Mead's medical
outlook was influenced by the science of astrology, as shown
in his treatise *Concerning the Influence of the Sun and Moon upon
Human Bodies, and the Diseases thereby produced*. Opinions
vary as to his capabilities as a physician ; but in the treatment
of small-pox, at any rate, he seems to have ignored the work
of Sydenham with consequent detriment to his practice, for
he was displaced in favour of Thomas Dover as physician to
some families of rank and fortune. However Mead's material
success is unquestionable ; and his literary taste and somewhat
cynical attitude towards medical practice are evident in the

---

[1] A. CASTIGLIONI, *A History of Medicine*, 1947, 656.
[2] RICHARD MEAD, *A Short Discourse concerning Pestilential Contagion and
Methods to be used to Prevent it*, 1720, 32.

following letter of advice to a young physician, Dr. Timothy Vanbustle :—

Should you have an itching to make your name known by writing a book on physic, yet so customary, I will advise you to choose the subject by which you think you will get most money ; or that will bring you the most general business, as fevers, smallpox, etc. . . . The method of writing, if in your frontispiece you address not your book to some great man, is to club with some other physicians ; and thus by way of letters to commend each other's good practice, and to support and make each other favour. But above all things, take particular care, let the subject be what it will, that the words be well chosen, so to make up an elegant and fervid speech ; since you have ten to one that mind the language more than the ideas.[1]

The strong literary bent amongst physicians, suggested in Mead's letter, is further exemplified in the lives of many of Dover's contemporaries. Sir Samuel Garth (1661–1714), poet and wit, was such a practitioner. His literary and social tastes overshadowed his medical activities, so that he never succeeded to any great extent as a physician, although his society was much courted by all the brilliant wits of his day. Likewise Dr. John Arbuthnot (1667–1735) combined literature and medicine. In a series of political pamphlets he popularized the name of " John Bull " as the representative Englishman, and was as much at ease in literary circles, which included Pope, Swift, Gay, and Parnell, as he was at the bedside of his patients. More versatile was Dr. John Freind (1675–1728), who achieved some measure of success as classical scholar, chemist, politician, military historian, medical historian, and courtier-physician. Another physician, Sir Richard Blackmore (1650–1724), was a prolific though minor poet, and Sir John Hill's reputation as a dramatist earned him the following epigram :—

> For physic and farces
> His equal there scarce is
> His farces are physic
> His physic a farce is.[2]

Thomas Dover, who was no great scholar, would have little in common with many of the leaders of his profession.

---

[1] JOHN NICHOLS, *Literary Anecdotes of the 18th Century*, 1812, Vol. IV, 219
[2] F. B. WINSLOW, *Physic and Physicians*, 1852, Vol. I, 211.

Like Sydenham he was essentially a practical man, averse to the bookish approach to clinical problems, which was then too fashionable. Dover's background, education, and writing all seem to suggest that he had more in common with earlier physicians, such as Radcliffe and Sydenham, than with his own more scholarly contemporaries : for at that time even physicians with a more scientific bent preferred the study of natural science to that of clinical medicine.

Dr. John Fothergill amassed a large collection of stuffed animals, exotic plants, corals, shells, and insects : and Sir Hans Sloane was a lifelong botanist, although his early enthusiasm for natural history is said to have earned Sydenham's rebuke. Shortly after qualification, Sloane visited Jamaica as physician to the Governor, and whilst there he made a unique collection of specimens which later, together with many books and manuscripts, helped to found the British Museum. Sloane succeeded Sir Isaac Newton as President of the Royal Society, and, with the fruits of his highly remunerative practice, he purchased the manor of Chelsea, where his name is perpetuated in Sloane Square and Hans Place.

These learned physicians frequently clashed in medical polemics ; they thrived on disputations, and as one would expect, their pamphlets were invariably well written, often studded with epigrams, and usually robustly witty, revealing their scholarly rather than scientific tastes. Too often they contented themselves, either by upholding their arguments on the authority of the classical physicians, or by merely pouring ridicule (and indeed often outright abuse) upon their antagonists. Thus, medical discussion was often hampered by an unbecoming spirit of acrimony. Dr. Wynter, for example, addressed the following verses to Dr. Cheyne, a corpulent Scottish physician, as a protest against the latter's suggestion of dietary moderation, in contrast to the current habit of excessive indulgence :—

> Tell me from whom, fat headed Scot,
> Didst thou thy system learn.
> From Hippocrates thou hadst it not,
> Nor Celsus nor Pitcairn.

Suppose we own that milk is good
And say the same of grass ;
The one for babes is only food
The other for an ass.[1]

A bitter controversy, which eventually led to a duel, followed the publication of Dr. Freind's book on fevers. His views were attacked by Dr. Woodward, Gresham Professor of Physic. Freind, supported by Mead, had recommended a purge during the second fever of confluent small-pox, whereas Woodward, who had a hypothesis about " the biliose salts " of the stomach, advocated an emetic instead. Arbuthnot also joined in the fray, and contributed two pamphlets in which he ridiculed Woodward's biliose salts, but at times his humour was marred by coarseness. An eminent layman, Sir Richard Steele, replied with two pamphlets in Dr. Woodward's favour, in which he rightly pointed out that Woodward's critics had merely poured contempt upon their opponent without in any way effectively discussing their differences. But appeals to moderation and objectivity were ignored, and the squabble moved to its indecorous climax on June 19th, 1714, when a scuffle (rather than a duel) took place between Woodward and Mead in the courtyard of the College of Physicians. The *Weekly Journal* of the following day gives Dr. Woodward's version of the incident. It appears that Mead struck Woodward as he was entering the College, whereupon swords were drawn. After a few trivial thrusts, Woodward tripped and fell, thus Mead was able to wrench his sword away, but before he could demand an apology from his fallen adversary, the onlookers intervened and separated the two antagonists.

Such was the metropolitan medical scene which greeted the return of Thomas Dover. The long era of the learned, dilettante physician was drawing to its close ; but not without a final flourish. Fashionable practice brought handsome profits and social favour on an unprecedented scale. Successful physicians lived in splendour. They were robust individualists, often flamboyant in manner, forthright in speech, and seldom missed an opportunity of tilting a lance at a colleague.

---

[1] F. B. WINSLOW, *Physic and Physicians*, 1852, Vol. II, 60.

Medicine alone was too shallow to absorb all their energies, and coffee-house practice afforded ample leisure for their erudition to flower in other fields. But medical discussion was theoretical, and diagnoses were too often detached from the patient; blistering, purging, vomiting, and bleeding, wittily dismissed by Molière in *Le Malade Imaginaire* a century earlier, were still the order of the day : for it was the baroque age in medicine, a time of physick in the grand manner.

CHAPTER XII

A PHYSICIAN OF VARYING FORTUNE

A heavy weight of hours has chained and bowed
One too like thee : tameless, and swift and proud.

SHELLEY

SHORTLY after receiving his share of the profits from the voyage Thomas Dover again set out on his travels. This time he crossed Europe to Asia Minor, but the nature of this journey has not been fully revealed. It was probably a holiday, although at least one of the observations he made during his journey was to influence his subsequent practice. This was a visit to the Hungarian quicksilver mines where he saw " slaves working entirely naked to prevent them stealing the metal ".[1] But they dodged their masters " by swallowing every day so much mercury that they could buy a choppin of drink with it at night ".[2] These travels seem to have taken him as far as Smyrna whence he voyaged to England.

On his return Thomas Dover settled in London, where he continued to treat the occasional illness amongst his friends and acquaintances. At this time it is evident that he regarded his small practice as a hobby, rather than a serious occupation, as he still thought it unnecessary to become a licentiate of the College of Physicians. But in 1720, when a particularly severe epidemic of small-pox swept the metropolis, Thomas Dover emerged from obscurity, and within a remarkably short time his successful treatment of this disease had brought him into prominence amongst people of influence. Viscountess

---

[1] THOMAS DOVER, *The Ancient Physician's Legacy*, 1742, 74.

[2] Dover again refers to his Continental travels when he writes, " The ladies of Smyrna often take quicksilver as a remedy against barrenness ". *The Ancient Physician's Legacy*, 3rd ed., 47.

Dupplin described Dover's unusual treatment of small-pox in a letter to her aunt, Abigail Harley, Countess of Oxford :—

There is a famous man in town called now a doctor, who undertakes to cure the smallpox a new way ; I believe you may have heard of him by the name of Captain Dover. He came here with the Agripulca ship in the Queen's time. His method for the aforesaid distemper is quick-silver and the cold bath. At this time he has under his care Lady Louisa Berkeley ; her grandmother, the Duchess of Richmond, dismissed Doctor Chamberlain, and sent for this famous man. Lady Mildred Hotham turned off Mead, and Hulst, and sent for him to her daughter, Mrs. Corbett. The Dutchess of Devonshire turned off Mead and Freind, and sent for him to Lady Rachel Manners. None of these ladies were given over by the physicians, which amazes all reasonable people that they should be put into such a quack's hands. I believe next post I may send you word that they are dead, I could not hear today that they were. I heard Mrs. Corbett had lost the sight of her eyes, not in the manner others do in the smallpox, for the first thing Dover does is to strike it all in, but she is irrevocably blind.[1]

This letter is of great interest for, although the writer is pessimistic about Dover's ability, and indeed regards him as a " quack ", she nevertheless does record that he was trusted by intelligent and influential people who had dismissed in his favour the services of four leading Fellows of the College of Physicians, each of whom was later destined for royal patronage. This incident, with its aftermath, was, I believe, one of the main reasons which later prompted Dover's bitter attacks on the Faculty of Physicians.

Of more importance is the suggestion that Dover was employing a novel form of treatment, which is aptly expressed by the term " he strikes it all in ". This phrase suggests that Dover's treatment was an endeavour to keep the eruption (and presumably the temperature) within reasonable bounds, rather than to encourage a rapid manifestation of pustules (which was the orthodox view) in the hope of thereby ridding the body of the actual elements of disease.

Another letter from the Reverend Thomas Mangey, chaplain to the Bishop of London, to Dr. Waller gives a more detailed description of Dover's treatment :—

---

[1] *Harley Papers*, Letter from Viscountess Dupplin to Abigail Harley, March 4th, 1720, Vol. XXXIV, ff. 192a, 192b.

I am glad of this opportunity of Kissing your hand and telling you something in your profession which is the whole talk of the town.   The smallpox for these two months hath raged here more universally and fatally than for some years past ; which hath occasioned some reflections upon the most eminent physicians, especially Dr. Mead and Dr. Freind who have affected some singularity in their practice upon that distemper. But one Dr. Dover, a man unknown to the faculty and who hath been a sea captain for many years, hath contributed very greatly to the diminution of their reputation.   He was accidentally called in to one Mrs. Corbot, who had been given over by Dr. Mead, who said she would die in a few hours.   This new doctor affirmed she was murdered by the Physicians, ordered the blisters (being six in number) to be taken off, sends for an operator, and with some difficulty persuades him to take as much blood as he could, which amounted to sixteen ounces.   He then takes her out of bed, and orders her clean linen, after that gives her a large draught of sherry, orange and water, which operated so well that in two hours time she showed the signs of recovery, and is now in a very hopeful way.   He hath observed the same method with like success with several persons of quality this week, and is as yet in very great vogue.   He pretends to have learnt the method of cure in the West Indies where no one is known to die of the smallpox ; and only saith that a greater quantity of blood is to be taken away here, upon account of more luxurious living.   He declaims against his bretheren of the faculty with public and great vehemence ; and particularly against purging and blistering in the distemper which he affirms to be the death of thousands.[1]

It is evident that Thomas Dover's treatment was virtually the cooling method advocated by Sydenham, which had then fallen into disfavour.   Although Sydenham slightly modified his method to suit the needs of the particular patient, he always endeavoured to keep them ambulant, and on a light diet with plenty of fluids in the early stages of small-pox : later, he often bled them, and invariably prevented excessive sweating by exposing the patient's body to the air.   Likewise, Dover's treatment with copious fluids, bleeding, and cooling baths is essentially similar to Sydenham's method, and is still in accordance with the present conception of the symptomatic treatment of small-pox.   Modern textbooks recommend the application of face masks soaked in cold water, and tepid baths once or twice daily to counter the intense skin irritation, together with copious fluids in order to correct dehydration.

---

[1] Letter from Thomas Mangey to Dr. Waller, March 4th, 1720.   JOHN NICHOLS, *Literary Anecdotes*, 1812, Vol. I, 135.

Purging and blistering, previously administered by Mead, would lead to further dehydration, hæmoconcentration, prolonged pyrexia, and would only serve to aggravate the intense skin irritation of the eruptive stage. Dover's treatment (whether intentional or otherwise) had, in the light of present knowledge, the merits of a more rational basis. He tried to correct the dehydration, endeavoured to reduce the temperature, eased the skin irritation, and (as septicæmia and cardiac failure are two of the common complications of small-pox) also found bleeding of value.

But Dover and Sydenham (though essentially similar in method) used the cooling treatment in varying degree, and for entirely different reasons. Sydenham regarded small-pox as an inevitable process to which almost every one was subject once, at least, in his lifetime. Therefore his main object was to assist a natural process. To this end he introduced his cooling regimen so that the eruption would appear on the fourth day, " which is the natural and proper time ".[1] Furthermore, by stressing the importance of a slower development of the pustules, he suggests that his aim in keeping the patient cool was to facilitate a more complete removal of the elements of disease—the pustules. " I am very sure that the slower the pustules come out," he says, " the more general the separation of the variolous matter will be, the better they will ripen, and the less danger there will be of them striking in : whereas if they be driven out too soon, the matter, being yet crude and indigested, is precipitated, and deceives our expedition, like over early fruit."[2]

Thomas Dover implies a different reason for using the cooling treatment, as when condemning the application of blisters he mentions the importance of " diluting the blood " : " Cantharides, which is not only poison and inflames the Fluids, but drains off the purer Part of the Blood, which is the serum. By this Practice the Mass becomes more grumous and thick ; so that Circulation is impeded, and the Patient suffocated : Whereas if there was Care taken to dilute and

---

[1] *Entire Works of Thomas Sydenham*, 1753, 118.   Ed. John Swann.
[2] *Ibid.*, 119.

thin the Mass of Blood, Circulation would be much easier maintain'd and by this Means prevent Death."[1]   Another difference is that whereas Sydenham tended to use his cooling treatment for small-pox, Dover extended its use to other fevers : " In all other Fevers I prescribe the cool Regimen," he says, " which must be follow'd in case Mankind prefer Life to Death, Ease to Pain ; a short Fit of Illness to a long and tedious one ; a good, to a broken and shatter'd Constitution ; laying aside Blisters, and all heating and poisonous Powders ; The former serve only to keep the Patient upon the Rack ; the latter, to heighten and increase his Fever— And what is still worse it extracts the Serum, which is the purest Part of the Blood."[2]

Modesty was definitely not one of Thomas Dover's qualities. On the contrary, he was brimming over with all the vaingloriousness of exuberant vitality ; and so easily was he animated in the recital of his exploits, both martial and medical, that he eagerly sought out every opportunity of exploiting his success to the detriment of others. His conceit, which is quite apparent when recounting the details of the following case, was later partly responsible for his undoing. " Miss Corbett had as high a confluent smallpox as ever I saw," writes Dover, " making bloody water and the worst symptoms attending her. Dr. Mead and another physician left her saying she could not live six hours. I was called to her. I desired she might instantly be blooded, The Right Honourable The Lady Hotham, her Mother, sent for a surgeon who refused to do it, telling My Lady that Dr. Mead said, that if she was blooded she would die instantly. I told my lady that ' colours were all the same to the blind '. I had a *black man* who blooded very well, and sent for him who performed the operation. She lost a vast quantity of blood. Miss Corbett declared afterwards that upon bleeding she found her spirits revived, and as it were a new life coming on and so it pleased God she recovered."[3]

---

[1] THOMAS DOVER, *The Ancient Physician's Legacy*, 1742, 6th ed., 105.

[2] *Ibid.*, 104.

[3] *Ibid.*, 120.

Following his initial success in the treatment of small-pox Thomas Dover rapidly acquired a fashionable practice ; but his overbearing attitude fostered a malicious rumour (started, he says, by the apothecaries) to the effect that by introducing a new method of treatment he had caused the death of the Duke of Rutland, Lord Irwin, and Mr. Mansel " of the great Welsh family ",[1] none of whom had, in fact, been his patients. The reason for Dover's forthright condemnation of the treatment of others, by such expressions as " she was murdered by the Physicians", was probably due to his mistaken notion of the true mortality of confluent small-pox. His master, Sydenham, had taught that small-pox was only a mild disease, the mortality from which could be attributed to the doctor's faulty treatment. This belief was further strengthened by his own observations in Jamaica where alastrim, which he regarded as true small-pox, was not a fatal disease. Thus by teaching and observation, it seems that Dr. Dover was snared into a false conclusion, which he upheld with characteristic tenacity against the attacks of his contemporaries.

The details of Dover's treatment during the small-pox epidemic of 1720 are stressed for many reasons. They demonstrate that treatment of fevers (the largest part of eighteenth-century medicine) was the keystone on which he founded his metropolitan practice ; and also, by his unorthodox method, reveals his first conflict with professional colleagues, whom he later denounced in the strongest terms. But of more consequence is the fact that by successfully practising Sydenham's treatment Thomas Dover stood alone, under the changing fashion of the times. " I am very sensible, my method in curing fevers is much exploded," he says, " because I act quite contrary to common practise." Dover's boundless confidence in his own ability and in soundness of his method is evident from the following challenge—" I defy the malice of my most implacable enemies," he says, " to make it appear that in my last ten years' (1722–1732) practice, I have lost twelve patients in all kinds of fevers put together."[2]

---

[1] THOMAS DOVER, *The Ancient Physician's Legacy*, 6th ed., 1742, 140.
[2] *Ibid.*, 144.

At this time (1720-1) Thomas Dover lived at Cecil Street, off the Strand. The metropolis of his day was shaped rather like a dumb-bell, with the cities of London and Westminster at either end, connected by the Strand. Cecil Street was therefore equally well placed for either professional visits to Westminster, or business deals in the City, which was then seething with gossip of the South Sea stock—for 1720 was the peak year of that unfortunate enterprise. Eager speculators from every walk of life daily left their regular occupations and hastened to Exchange Alley, where their expressions reflected the state of their fortunes. Thomas Dover, as a substantial shareholder in the South Sea Company, would be a frequent visitor. It is not known whether he invested in other stock; for the South Sea Company happened to be only the most gigantic bubble in a sea of bubbles. Numerous smaller companies, many with extravagant projects, flourished for a few weeks and then vanished completely. One of the best known " bubble companies "[1] was " Puckle's Machine Company ",[2] which proposed to revolutionize the art of war by making a machine for discharging round and square cannon balls and bullets. Another concern proposed a wheel for perpetual motion; yet perhaps the most preposterous of all was " a company for carrying on an undertaking of great advantage, but nobody to know what it is ".[3] Nevertheless, subscribers were found amongst the credulous and avaricious public for even the most bizarre ventures.

But enterprise, like Icarus, had soared too high. In order to bolster public confidence, the directors of the South Sea Company paid out bribes totalling £1,250,000 to public men; and to get the premiums to pay for these bribes, they issued unsanctioned stock. Later in August, 1720 the South Sea Company took out writs against many of the ' bubble' concerns (as they were not legally incorporated as public companies) in order to stifle their competition. This led to an immediate fall in stock; but a few weeks later, when it was rumoured that the South Sea Company was about to

---

[1,2] CHARLES MACKAY, *Memoirs of Extraordinary Popular Delusions*, 1841, Vol. I, 100.

[3] E. A. BENIANS, *Cambridge Modern History*, 1904, Ch. VI, 177.

combine with the Bank of England, the shares soared again to six hundred and seventy-five by the beginning of September. But when the rumour proved to be false, public confidence finally gave way to distrust, and a week later the stock had crashed to one hundred and seventy-five. Fortunes were swept away overnight; and thereafter the shares gradually dwindled away, although a committee to investigate the scandal was not appointed until the following June. After the crash Defoe writes :—

You may now at a tavern have a mutton cutlet broil'd by Blowsabella, the kitchen damsel, without being teaz'd with her enquiries of what new subscriptions are come out that day. You may go to the coffee house and call for a dish of tea or coffee and have it without difficulty, whereas if you said " Jack, give me a dish of Bohea," he would presently say—without taking notice of what you call'd for—" Sir, will you buy a thousand pounds stock in rock salt, or the grand fishery ", and so on, thro' all the rest. If you came not to his price, the blue apron'd dog would cry, " Sir, I'll give you a thousand pound a share for as many as you will bring me ", and so in proportion for any bubble that was afoot.[1]

Thomas Dover's original investment must have been at least £6000, so at times he had been fabulously wealthy— on paper. When stock was low, but before the government ordered an inquiry, Dover made further investments in the hope of mitigating this sudden change of fortune. He raised the necessary capital by mortgaging his estate at Barton : but at the same time, he probably realized that a loss of some degree was inevitable, as he turned once more to medicine— this time as a means of livelihood.

On January 6th, 1721, he first applied for admission to the College of Physicians, and was summoned to appear with his Cambridge diplomas at the next meeting of the Censors. But in April he wrote from Cambridge, to inform Sir Hans Sloane, that as the Vice-Chancellor was away, he had been unable to get his diplomas, and therefore begged to be excused from appearing.

The Registrar of the College of Physicians must have been under the impression that Dover was a Doctor of Medicine,

---

[1] DANIEL DEFOE, quoted from CHARLES MACKAY, *Memoirs of Extraordinary Popular Delusions*, 1841, Vol. I, 104.

as the first two entries in the College annals refer to " Dr.
Dover " ; but on May 5th it is recorded that " Mr. Dover "
appeared before the Censors with a testimonial for the degree
of " Batchelor of Physick ".[1]

At this meeting he was informed that he could not be
considered for a Fellowship of the College, but could only be
examined for admission as a licentiate, which would enable
him to practise in London. Dover agreed, and passed his
first examination in physiology. The examinations for the
licence of the college, though probably a formality in the case
of university graduates, would nevertheless be a somewhat
irksome undertaking for a man of sixty, with thirty-five years'
clinical experience. Therefore, throughout the greater part
of 1721 Dover was occupied with monthly examinations.
On June 2nd he was approved in pathology ; a month later in
therapeutics ; and, by an ironical stroke of fortune, he was
finally examined in medicine by Dr. Hulse whom he had but
lately displaced as physician to Lady Hotham. On September
30th, the examinations came to an end, and ' Mr. Thomas
Dover ', having been proposed by Sir Hans Sloane as a
licentiate of the College of Physicians, gave his oath of
allegiance, was duly balloted, elected, and admitted ; but,
as " one of the Keys being wanting to come at the Seal ",[2]
he was unable to receive his diploma until the following
day.

Between depressing visits to Exchange Alley, Thomas
Dover was now free to practise with impunity. He was an
unorthodox practitioner, as is already evident from his
treatment of small-pox ; but yet another novel feature of his
practice was quicksilver treatment, which he favoured in an
increasing number of ailments. A robust independent spirit,
Dr. Dover practised his own way, indifferent to the views of
his colleagues ; but although, as a Licentiate of the College
of Physicians, he was entitled to certain professional privileges,
he was also expected to conform to the regulations of that
body. But Dover was as violent in his prejudices as he was

---

[1] *Annals of Royal College of Physicians*, 1721, May 5, Vol. VIII, 154.
[2] *Ibid.*, 1721, September 30, Vol. VIII, 175.

firm in his own views : one of his strongest aversions being
to the use of blisters.

"An eminent physician, when asked how blistering came
so much a fashion, he answered they had it from the Indians.
But I," says Dover with a characteristic flourish, " that have
seen more Indians than all the physicians in England, deny
that the Indians ever make use of blisters."[1]   Apart from the
fact that blisters drew off the serum, which Dover considered
to be " the purest part of the blood ", his other objection to
their use was simply because he held that blistering was an
unnecessarily painful procedure, and in support of this view
he mentions Radcliffe and Sydenham : " I should be glad
to know if Dr. Radcliffe ever used this inhuman method of
blistering, as it is now in vogue.   I should be glad to know
likewise if there is any authority from any of our most
approved authors for such a practice.   The honest Dr.
Sydenham calls blistering ' Humano cario ludere '."[2]

Such was Dover's distaste for this form of treatment that
when called to see a patient on whom blisters had been
applied, he immediately tore them off and passed scathing
remarks on the ability of the physician who had applied
them.

It was due to such an incident that Dr. Wagstaffe, a Fellow
of the College, complained of Dover's behaviour to the
Committee of Censors, charging him with a breach of the
moral statutes.   Thus on February 2nd, 1722, barely five
months after his election as a licentiate, Thomas Dover was
summoned to answer the charge before Sir Hans Sloane and
the College Censors.   Wagstaffe stated that Dover had
attended a patient with erysipelas whom he had also been
treating.   Whereupon, Dover had not only refused to meet
him in consultation, but had taken off blisters, removed
forty ounces of blood, and had generally found fault with
all former treatment.   The son of the deceased patient, an
apothecary, confirmed most of Dr. Wagstaffe's evidence.   He
was, however, unable to state that Dover had definitely refused

---

[1] THOMAS DOVER, *The Ancient Physician's Legacy*, 1742, 6th ed., 105.
[2] *Ibid.*, 106.

to meet Dr. Wagstaffe, although he had insisted on his own methods, and " had made no offer to meet him ".[1]

When called to answer these accusations, Dover said that he had been asked to see the patient by Sir John Blunt, and was unaware of the previous attendance of Dr. Wagstaffe, against whom he had designed no injury. However, the President and Censors decided that he had " plainly transgressed the moral Statutes, but that they would pass it over this time, admonishing him against such proceedings for the Future ".[2]

Although Dover had merely been admonished, this incident soon became coffee-house gossip, and had an adverse effect on his practice which now, like his investments, gradually began to dwindle away. By another indiscretion Dover had again antagonized both physicians and apothecaries ; and the latter were well able to retaliate by simply not recommending patients to his care. It is highly likely that Dover had developed a distaste for the Faculty of Physicians from his early days as Sydenham's pupil, as his great teacher seemed to have had many enemies in the college, and never succeeded to a fellowship.

Gideon Harvey, Physician-in-Ordinary to Charles II, was another eminent physician who was never elected a Fellow, and remained a bitter critic of the Faculty throughout his life. Patronage and unctuous loyalty counted for much in those days ; but although there were certain cliques in the college who were perhaps unfairly prejudiced, Dover had no grounds for complaint as he could never attain to a fellowship without a doctorate in medicine. Indeed, his recent admonition was well justified, as he had plainly transgressed one of the moral statutes of the college, which later, when attacking that institution, he took the trouble to translate from the Latin : " A Physician, who is called to a Patient as a Second, shall by no means cause the former to be rejected, neither shall he make any Innovations in the Practice (extreme cases excepted) before he shall have consulted with him ; and to prevent all occasions of Frauds of this kind, whosoever is sent for to a Sick Person, shall first enquire of the Patient, or

---

[1], [2] *Annals of Royal College of Physicians*, 1722, January 5, Vol. VIII, 200.

Bystanders, whether any Physician has already prescribed, under penalty of twenty shillings."[1]

Dover's attitude towards the College of Physicians was well known, as one of his critics, Dr. Turner, writes: " I never was call'd in upon Him, nor, should I care to meet a Man in Consultation, who had behaved so unhandsomely to the whole Faculty of Physick, even to those very Gentlemen who did him the Honour to admit him a Licentiate."[2]

Shortly after his admonition at the College of Physicians, Thomas Dover gave up his London practice which had started so well, and returned to Barton-on-the-Heath. There his wife died; and in addition to his bereavement and failure in practice, he was also constantly plagued by creditors. His investments in the South Sea Company were now beyond resuscitation, and in order to meet his liabilities he was forced to sell his estates. Accordingly on May 6th, 1727, an indenture was drawn up, whereby Thomas Dover, " doctor in physick ", agreed to the sale of his house, lands, and farm buildings, to Thomas Mander of the Inner Temple for the sum of £3400. Mander agreed to pay immediately certain debts owing from the estate, including £800 to the South Sea Company, and the discharge of a mortgage of £1037 10s. It was also agreed that the balance of £1562 10s. was to be paid to Dover by September 29th on " pain of forfeiture ".[3]

After all debts had been paid from the estate only £140 remained for Dover's use until the balance was due. Therefore in May, 1727 Thomas Dover had reached the nadir of his chequered career, as he was then widowed, homeless, and virtually bankrupt.

But nearby at Stanway Hall in Gloucestershire lived Dover's kinsman, Robert Tracy. A firm friendship existed between them and it was to Robert Tracy that Dover later dedicated his *The Ancient Physician's Legacy*. The Tracys, who claimed descent from the Saxon Kings of England, had been granted Stanway at the dissolution of the monasteries; but

---

[1] THOMAS DOVER, *The Ancient Physician's Legacy*, 1742, 6th ed., 232.

[2] DANIEL TURNER, *The Ancient Physician's Legacy Surveyed*, 1733, 2.

[3] *Indenture between Thomas Dover and Thomas Mander*, 1727, May 6th, Royal College of Surgeons Library.

the spacious and elegant manor house where Dover now resided, dated from the reign of James I. However, Thomas Dover was not long permitted to enjoy the leisurely life of an eighteenth-century squire, as his professional services were in great demand during a severe epidemic of fever which raged with varying virulence throughout the whole two years of his residence at Stanway. Unfortunately he does not name the fever, but during these years there was a great increase in the death rate throughout the whole country due to frequent and severe outbreaks of small-pox. " I happened to live in Gloucestershire ", he says, " during the years 1728 and 1729 when a very fatal Epidemical fever raged in such degree, as to sweep off whole families, nay almost whole villages. I was called to several homes where eight or nine persons were down at a time ; yet did not so much as lose one patient where I was concerned."[1]

After two years at Stanway Thomas Dover returned to Bristol where he again tried to establish himself in practice. This time his efforts were not very successful, as shortly after his arrival there he wrote to Sir Hans Sloane asking him to recommend patients to his care :—

Being now settl'd at this Place, I beg y^r Favour you'd recommend y^r Patients y^u find this way to my Care. I should not have ye Confidence to presume thus far, had y^u not honor'd me in several Consultations wherein We never failed of Success which was much owing to y^r superior judgment. 'Tis possible y^u may prevail wth some other Gentlemen of y^r Profession to honour me with a Character y^t may incline Their Patients to make use of me likewise, in doing this—you'd very much Oblige

Sir
Y^r Ever Faithfull
Humble Servt
Tho. Dover.[2]

Evidently Thomas Dover was still on friendly, though respectful, terms with Sir Hans Sloane ; their acquaintance probably dating from their early apprenticeship with Sydenham, or even later during their stay in Jamaica. It also seems that Sir Hans Sloane had confidence in Dover, as it is evident that he had already recommended some patients

[1] THOMAS DOVER, *The Ancient Physician's Legacy*, 1742, 6th ed., 144.
[2] *Sloane MSS.*, 4046, f. 255, B.M.

to his care. In another letter from Bristol Dover consults Sloane about a dangerously-ill patient, and also asks for an appointment with him in London.

But Thomas Dover never really settled again in Bristol, and whilst awaiting a flow of patients he began writing a medical book. When this book was published in 1732 he had left Bristol and, at the age of seventy, was ready for another venture as a London physician.

CHAPTER XIII

THE ANCIENT PHYSICIAN'S LEGACY

The first physicians by debauch were made,
Excess began, and sloth sustained the trade ;
By chase our long-liv'd fathers earned their food,
Toil strung their nerves and purified their blood ;
But we, their sons, a pamper'd race of men,
Are dwindled down to three score years and ten.

DRYDEN

WHEN his book was published in 1732 Thomas Dover was practising from Lombard Street in the City, where he " had been settled eighteen months ".[1] Although he occasionally refers to classical and contemporary medical works, his book was primarily designed for popular appeal ; as such it met with immediate success. It was a sort of eighteenth-century *Family Physician* which, in the words of one of his correspondents, " made a great noise in London, and was the subject of almost every coffee house ".[2] The book was quite small (only one hundred and fifty pages of text), followed by many letters from grateful patients, and bore the long and pompous title, *The Ancient Physician's Legacy to his Country, being what he has collected in Forty-Nine Years' Practice : or, An Account of the Several DISEASES incident to Mankind, described in so Plain a Manner, that any Person may know the Nature of his own Disease. Together with Several Remedies for each Distemper, faithfully set down.*

The writing of medical essays and pamphlets for popular consumption was then quite common. One of the best of such books was George Cheyne's *Essay on Health and Long*

---

[1] THOMAS DOVER, *To the Author o " The Use and Abuse of Mercury"*, 1733, 5.

[2] THOMAS DOVER, *The Ancient Physician's Legacy*, 1742, 6th ed., 39.

Life ;[1] but most of the others fell far short of his standard, and were sweepingly dismissed by Luttram as " all bad and many dishonest ". His condemnation was probably merited, as most popular medical books were written solely for mercenary reasons,[2] or as Smollett puts it, " to force a trade ", rather than with the object of furthering medical knowledge. On such matters Smollett could write with some authority, as with his *Essay on the External Use of Water*[3] he had hoped to establish himself in fashionable practice. There is every reason to believe that Thomas Dover's book was also written for " revenue purposes ", and in order to enhance his reputation in the metropolis. Mr. Bradley, one of Dover's critical contemporaries, was also of the same opinion, as he condemned the whole book, except for the title-page where he says, " I met with the best piece of Learning and Philosophy . . . viz. price five shillings ; and I'm informed has had the desired Effect ".[4]

At the outset Dover makes no claim as a stylist. " I am very sensible ", he writes, " that my stile is not correct " :[5] but in spite of this unusual modesty his writing is characterized by a forthright sincerity. The contrast between Dover's book and modern medical works is remarkable. In order to be objective, the modern medical writer submerges his personality and presents us only with his name, qualifications, and appointments : whereas the *Ancient Physician's Legacy* endows us with the author's forceful character, interspersed amongst a description of forty-two diseases. He emerges as a disciple of " the honest Dr. Sydenham " with a genuine affection for his old Master ; as the swaggering champion of Guayaquil ; as a public benefactor denouncing the apothecaries' ill gotten gains ; as the very Luther of Medicine in open revolt against the hierarchy of physicians : and throughout the whole book

---

[1] GEORGE CHEYNE, *An Essay on Health and Long Life*, 1724, 1st ed.
[2] LUTTRAM, quoted by SIR WILLIAM OSLER, *Johns Hopk. Hosp. Bull.*, 1896, **7**, 6.
[3] TOBIAS SMOLLETT, *An Essay on the External Use of Water etc.*, 1752.
[4] H. BRADLEY, *Physical and Philosophical Remarks on Dr. Dover's Late Pamphlet*, 1733, 233.
[5] THOMAS DOVER, *The Ancient Physician's Legacy*, 1742, 6th ed., 2.

runs the piquant flavour of self-advertisement. Many letters from grateful patients are inserted, all attesting to the author's great skill. Therefore, in several respects Dover's book was a typical product of his day, and as such it should be viewed.

Two editions were published by Bellesworth and Hitch in 1732, and five editions in the following year. The second and third editions published " for the relict of the late R. Bradly, F.R.S. " were probably pirated, as in the frontispiece the author's name is misspelt " Thomas Dovar, M.D. ", whereas in all editions published by Bellesworth and Hitch his name and qualifications are correctly presented. The book, which went to eight editions (the last in 1771, twenty-nine years after the author's death), was also translated into French and enjoyed a wide circulation on the Continent. The reason for the book's success is not hard to seek ; it was pungently critical, yet offered many useful prescriptions and novel forms of treatment, the whole being well spiced with anecdotes.

Many of Dover's criticisms were well justified. The theory of " Signatures ", much pressed by Paracelsus, still held sway. Its advocates administered medicines prepared from plants which had some characteristics in common with the disease they treated. In this belief liverwort was often given for diseases of the liver, real or imaginary ; and plants with heart-shaped leaves were considered suitable for cardiac disorders. Thus when discussing the treatment of jaundice, Dover criticizes Paracelsus for recommending the " inner bark of tarberries, tarmerick, rhubarbs and all plants of a yellow cast ".[1] He further condemns the use of *Arbor tremuli* for the ague, *trachelium* for quinsy, *Pulmonaria maculosa* for consumption, all of which he mentions to show " on what weak foundations we often venture our lives ".[2]

Also Dover condemns the revolting practice of prescribing bezoar stones, which was in fact beginning to decline at that time. Many stones were used of which the most esteemed was *Lapis bezoar orientale* from the Persian wild goat ; less expensive stones were obtained from apes, llamas, and the alpine chamois. They were merely calculi, usually obtained

---

[1,2] THOMAS DOVER, *The Ancient Physician's Legacy*, 1742, 6th ed., 52.

from the gall-bladder, and their special virtue was supposed
to be due to some mysterious plant on which the particular
animal thrived. Originally bezoar stones were used as an
antidote to poisons, but later they were given in many fevers
and skin conditions. They were included in the London
Pharmacopœia until 1746 and were sold for between £3 and
£5 an ounce.

Dover refers to bezoar as " That petrified Matter of
Disease cut out of the Paunches, Galls and Bladders of some of
the nastiest creatures in being, as Gucinanoes ; a monstrous
beast between a camel and a he goat ; black cattle ; hogs,
goats, and an ugly animal they call pacis, d'la Tierra monkeys,
porcupines, and all such nasty animals. We in dissections,
too often find in the galls and bladders of human bodies
great quantities of stones, which doubtless may as well serve
for BEZOAR as the diseased matters of the forementioned
beasts".[1]

Gascoyne's powder was another useless nostrum which,
says Dover, " occasions yearly the loss of many thousands of
subjects of the Crown ".[2] As he had previously demonstrated,
Dover was opposed to blistering in the treatment of small-pox ;
and he strongly protested against the common practice of
needlessly varying prescriptions in order to increase the
apothecaries' profit, and thereby gain his favour. His many
aversions were completed with a sweeping condemnation of
the whole Faculty of Physicians, " who like Moles work
underground, lest their practices should be discovered to the
Populace."[3]

But Thomas Dover's *Legacy* contains much more than a
criticism of professional bodies and outmoded nostrums.
He was a pioneer in fostering inoculation for small-pox, and
was equally fervent in his desire to popularize cold bathing,
which he recommended for many skin conditions. " But
why should men of art be so averse to cold bathing ? " he
asks. " The Israelites were famous for an itchy scabby people,
and the only remedy we find they made use of was an

---

[1] THOMAS DOVER, *The Ancient Physician's Legacy*, 1742, 6th ed., 106.
[2] *Ibid.*, 86.
[3] *Ibid.*, 241.

PLATE VII

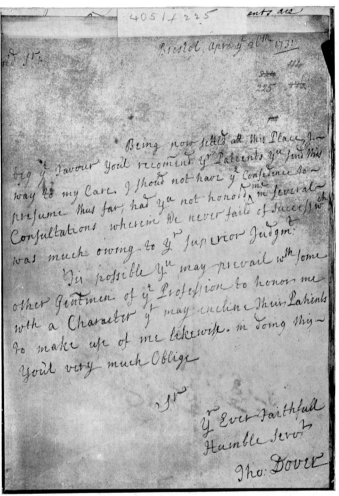

Letter from Thomas Dover to Sir Hans Sloane, April, 1731.

PLATE VIII

The Ancient
PHYSICIAN's
Legacy to his Country.
Being what he has collected himself,
In Fifty-eight Years PRACTICE:
Or, an Account of the several
DISEASES incident to MANKIND;
Described in so plain a Manner,

That any PERSON may know the
Nature of his own DISEASE.

Together with the several REMEDIES for each
DISTEMPER, faithfully set down.

Designed for the Use of all Private FAMILIES.

*Homines ad Deos, nullà in re propiùs accedunt, quàm
Salutem hominibus dando.
Homines ad Dæmones, nullà in re propius accedunt,
quàm Salutem hominibus negando.* Do.

By THOMAS DOVER, M. B.

The SIXTH EDITION.

In this EDITION are very considerable ADDITIONS; besides
a great Number of LETTERS sent from several Parts of
England, of the extraordinary CURES perform'd by Crude
MERCURY: With some Remarks on the Author of *The Use
and Abuse of Mercury*. To which is added, An ESSAY on
Midwifery; and the *Moral Characteristics* of the College of
Physicians, in *Latin* and *English*, by Way of Appendix;
together with a *Digression*.

LONDON:
Printed by H. KENT, for C. HITCH at the *Red-Lyon* in
Pater-Noster-Row; J. BROTHERTON at the *Bible*, next the
Fleece Tavern in *Cornhill*; and R. MINORS, in *St. Clement's*
Church-Yard, in the *Strand*. M.DCC.XLII.

Price stitch'd, Four Shillings.

Title-page of *The Ancient Physician's Legacy to His Country*, by Thomas
Dover, 6th edition, 1742.
(Wellcome Historical Medical Library.)

A
TREATISE
ON
MERCURY:

SHEWING

The Danger of taking it Crude for all
Manner of Disorders, after the present
Fashion, from its Nature, its Manner of
operating in the human Body, and Facts.

WITH SOME

Remarks on the *Antient Physician's Legacy*.

The SECOND EDITION.

To which are added,

A REPLY to the Remarks on the Treatise
of the Use and Abuse of Mercury, in the Fourth
Edition of Dr. *Dover's Antient Physician's Legacy*. Also an Answer to the *Antidote*, and
some Cases, collected since the First Edition;
with a Word or two of the *Mercurialists*.

*Nescem agere ignavus sinnet, abrotanum ægro
Non audet nisi qui didicit, dare.* HOR. L. 1. Ep.

LONDON:

Printed for J. ROBARTS, near the *Oxford-Arms* in
Warwick-Lane. M.DCC.XXXIII.

[Price One Shilling.]

Title-page of *A Treatise on Mercury; with some remarks on the "Ancient
Physician's Legacy"*, 2nd edition, 1733.
(Wellcome Historical Medical Library.)

immersion in cold water."[1] After denying that cold bathing, as suggested by other physicians, predisposed to pneumonia, Dover goes on to give the following physiological explanation of its healing properties. "Upon the patient's immersing in the most intense cold water that can possibly be found, all the heat is fleeing from the surface of the body, into its most inward parts. When the patient comes out, the heat returning from whence it came, performs its motion with that Elasticity and force, that it fills the skin with vast numbers of cutaneous spots, by which the blood becomes much finer and those corrupt parts of the fluids are discharged."[2]

Smollett's explanation of the beneficial effects of cold water are conveyed in similar terms. In his treatise, published twenty years after Dover's book, he strongly advocates cold bathing for all nervous diseases, urethral fistulæ, and "inveterate scropholous and scorbutic ulcers".[3]

Dover seems to have kept well abreast of medical knowledge, as in support of his treatment for small-pox he mentions the views of Boerhaave, who was then the leading physician in Europe. "I am credibly informed", he writes, "that the most learned and ingenious Dr. Boerhaave in all fevers bleeds plentifully, gives air to his patients; immediately tears off all blisters, and indulges the sick person with all manner of cooling and diluting liquors."[4]

After giving an adequate though brief description of the three types of small-pox, confluent, anomalous, and distinct, Dover describes a fourth variety which he calls the "spotted type". From his description, it would appear that this is what is now recognized as hæmorrhagic small-pox. "This sort begins with very high symptoms, and appears with large red spots, much like the confluent kind, with the face and other parts very much enflamed; yet in twelve hours the patient shall become perfectly pale, the very middle of those red spots turning to a black, conney substance, hardly so big as a large pin's head. Of this sort in forty-odd years' practice,

---

[1] Thomas Dover, *The Ancient Physician's Legacy*, 1742, 6th ed., 93.
[2] *Ibid.*, 93.
[3] Tobias Smollett, *An Essay on the External Use of Water etc.*, 1752, 6.
[4] Thomas Dover, *The Ancient Physician's Legacy*, 1742, 6th ed., 148.

I have observed no more than five, all children. I could never
carry one to the first critical day, whereas in the confluent
kind they rarely died before."[1]

Thomas Dover recommended bleeding (often excessive) in
the treatment of most infectious fevers. In cases of quinsy
he favoured high bleeding from the veins under the tongue,
as it was then thought that blood should be removed as near
as possible to the site of infection. He also bled patients with
pneumonia, erysipelas, and in the treatment of pulmonary
tuberculosis he prefers " frequent bleeding in small quantities "
to horse riding, as advocated by Sydenham.[2]

Although Dover often bled his patients excessively, he
was not given to indiscriminate bleeding in all febrile illnesses,
which was probably a legacy from Sydenham's teaching.
He considered that acute rheumatism (which he regarded as
a " high and inflammatory fever ") could be cured more
easily without bleeding ; and again in cases of measles and
scarlet fever, Dover shows admirable conservatism at a time
when over-treatment was common.

The bark (containing quinine) infused with a quart of red
port to which was added a few drops of liquid laudanum, still
seems an excellent remedy for malaria, although Mr. Bradley
suggested that it would only serve to make the patient drunk
and "inflame the blood".[3] Dover, unlike many of his
contemporaries, confined the use of quinine to the treatment of
malaria and certain nervous disorders, rather than exhibit the
drug indiscriminately as a general panacea. " Dr. Morton,
esteemed a good physician, was a great admirer of this
medicine ", he says, " insomuch that he gave it in almost all
cases. I never observed it do any good but in nervous
complaints."[4] He adds that in Peru, where the bark is
called Cascerilla, its only use is for the treatment of malaria,
which is in marked contrast to the state of affairs in England.
" It may be doubted if one hundredweight of it be used in a

---

[1] THOMAS DOVER, *The Ancient Physician's Legacy*, 1742, 6th ed., 31.

[2] *Ibid.*, 127.

[3] H. BRADLEY, *Physical and Philosophical Remarks on Dr. Dover's Late Pamphlet*, 1733, 48.

[4] THOMAS DOVER, *The Ancient Physician's Legacy*, 1742, 6th ed., 131.

whole year throughout that kingdome, which is more than twenty times as large as Great Britain."[1]

It is of interest to note that Dover regarded malaria as a disease of the nervous system, rather like epilepsy, as "it must proceed from the brain otherwise it is impossible to keep to its stated periods".[2] Although he failed to understand the aetiology of malaria, he had a good knowledge of the pathology of jaundice. Dover clinically differentiates symptomatic jaundice from obstructive jaundice ; the latter resulting from blockage of "the Ductus Choleclochus which leads from the gall to the intestine duodenum, the Bile not passing there leaves the Odure white, which otherwise takes its colour from it. But mixing with the blood, tinctures the skin, as the hair on the head or body takes its dye from the fluids".[3]

Evidently appendicitis (iliac passion) was quite common in Dover's day. He gives a good description of the condition, for which he suggests oral quicksilver and purging rather than vomiting, on the grounds that emetics would be more inclined to aggravate reversed peristalsis which he believed was the cause of the illness. When commenting on the danger of emetics in appendicitis, Dover hints at a knowledge of the physiology of digestion. " 'Tis considered the doctor many times gives satisfaction to the patient", he writes, " by showing the shiny matter that is brought off from the stomach, upon the point of feathers ; whereas that matter is necessary to promote digestion. Let it be considered for what end were these little cells formed in the Crusta Villosa."[4]

But Dover's book has many faults. It contains the occasional recipe from the age of alchemy ; his flimsy descriptions of disease are sometimes inaccurate, though invariably dogmatic. But more than any of the factual, clinical, or therapeutic errors, the author himself seems determined to provoke criticism by innumerable self-laudatory passages (excessive even by eighteenth-century standards), which are often at the expense of his professional

[1] THOMAS DOVER, The Ancient Physician's Legacy, 1742, 6th ed., 131.
[2] Ibid., 50.
[3] Ibid., 51.
[4] Ibid., 135.

colleagues. He misses no opportunity of blowing his own trumpet with a strident flourish, as when following an inadequate and erroneous account of ascites and dropsy, he dismisses the standard treatment of paracentesis abdominis and pompously asserts, " After all I shall venture to say, that let me but come to People as early in this Distemper as they generally apply for relief from other physicians, and it shall be cured with as much certainty as any other gentleman may cure a Distemper he thinks himself most master of ".[1] Again, Dover begins his discussion of the plague with a phrase more appropriate to the memoirs of a soldier of fortune than as part of a medical treatise, " When I took by storm the twin cities of Guiaquil, under the line, in the South Seas . . .".[2] Also, when discussing the importance of foreign travel as part of the necessary training of a physician, Dover again provokes the criticism of his colleagues by remarking that he has " travelled more than all the Physicians in Great Britain put together ".[3] As was only to be expected, such sallies of conceit provoked the raucous contempt of his colleagues, which was expressed in a series of pamphlets directing personal abuse against Dover, rather than criticizing his methods.

The Ancient Physician's Legacy also contains one revolting prescription for asthma. As an alternative to a mixture of black cherry, penny-royal, and rue, Dover recommends a dried toad, powdered and made into pills, which he says is an excellent remedy. He then digresses at some length (as was his frequent custom) in praise of toads, and of their value to medicine. His critics eagerly seized upon this aberration, and one of them crudely comments, " I can only say of our Nostrum-Monger, as the facetious Dr. Baynard said of his Dr. Stew-Toad, as he calls him, that he was one who set up for Miracle and Mystery ; and always makes Honey of a Dog's Tird : This martyrs more Toads than Popery has done Hereticks ".[4]

---

[1] THOMAS DOVER, The Ancient Physician's Legacy, 1742, 6th ed., 21.
[2] Ibid., 100.
[3] Ibid., 7.
[4] H. BRADLEY, Physical and Philosophical Remarks on Dr. Dover's Late Pamphlet, 1733, 14.

Dover never misses an opportunity of spicing his book with bizarre details of his travels. These digressions seem to serve the dual purpose of leavening the weight of medical facts and masking the author's ignorance of certain ailments. Hemiplegia, described in three lines, is followed by a simple discourse on the duplication of organs and their function throughout the body. This discussion is finally flavoured with the following anecdote of doubtful authenticity. " The Mahometan Women in the Greater Part of Asia ", he writes, " destroy one testicle ; no doubt they find their account in it because males make their addresses more frequently when there is less expense of spirits at each evacuation."[1]   As his critic Bradley comments, it is " a pretty sort of legacy for private Families ".[2]

Opinions vary as to whether traces of Sydenham's influence are discernible in *The Ancient Physician's Legacy*. But in many ways their works seem uncomparable. Sydenham's writings were meant to fashion a new approach to clinical problems, whereas Dover's book was merely a brief survey of disease designed for popular appeal in order to enhance its author's reputation. Yet Dover sincerely believed in all he wrote ; and although the descriptions of disease are scanty, his book undoubtedly bears Sydenham's stamp : not in the manner of clinical description, but rather from occasional hints, as in the treatment of fevers and of quinsy, from the use of opium, and the disinclination to over-treatment. It would also appear from the following popular discourse that the aim of Dover's treatment was always to aid a natural healing process, and such was the art of Sydenham, when he taught :—

Birds resort to their several sorts of castings when their stomachs are depraved ; in fevers to cold bathing, or when they have gorged themselves with too much food, then their weatherings on the tops of high trees. Let but a lady's lap-dog go out in the fields, he shall search everywhere to find the Garmen Canium, or Dog's Grass ; of which he shall eat till he both vomits and purges. . . . Providence has exempted us from the great benefit afforded to the subordinate creatures. If we have a fever, we must be kept close, and ply'd with the most heating remedies ; be deny'd

---

[1] THOMAS DOVER, *The Ancient Physician's Legacy*, 1742, 6th ed., 58.
[2] H. BRADLEY, *Physical and Philosophical Remarks on Dr. Dover's Late Pamphlet*, 1733, 32.

cooling and diluting liquors, and everything else that we call for with the greatest earnestness.   This is contradicting the rules of Nature, and most certainly wrong.   Right reason and the rules of Nature will eternally tally.[1]

Thomas Dover's book is now remembered for the powder which still bears his name.   Here is the original recipe :—

Take Opium one ounce, Salt-Petre and Tartar vitriolated each four ounces, Ipecacuanha one ounce, Liquorish one ounce.   Put the Salt-Petre and Tartar into a red-hot mortar, stirring them with a spoon until they have done flaming.   Then powder them very fine ; after that slice in your opium, grind them to a powder, and then mix the other powders with these.   Dose from forty to sixty or seventy grains in a glass of white wine Posset going to bed ; covering up warm and drinking a quart or three pints of the Posset—Drink while sweating.[2]

Though the essential constituents of his powder remain unchanged, Dover's quaint description, with its flavour of alchemy, has been considerably simplified in modern formularies.   The present dose of pulvis ipecacuanhæ et opii is 5-10 grains which contains 10 per cent of powdered ipecacuanha and opium made up with lactose.   With slight modifications, his powder also has a place in most foreign pharmacopœias.   Potassium sulphate is substituted for lactose in the Japanese Pharmacopœia, and the *Pharmacopée Française* recommends a maximum single dose of 15 grains together with a total of 60 grains during 24 hours.

A single dose of between 40 and 70 grains seemed unusually large even for those days, as Turner, commenting on the dangers of taking Dover's powder, adds that it contains the largest " dose of Opium that ever was prescrib'd by any one before him ".[3]   But Dover was quite confident of his powder, and was well aware that the high dose of opium he had recommended would be adequately buffered when combined with ipecacuanha.   He therefore answered his critics with grim humour—" Some Apothecaries have desired their Patients to make their Wills, and Settle their Affairs, before they venture upon so large a Dose as I have recommended,

---

[1] THOMAS DOVER, *The Ancient Physician's Legacy*, 1742, 6th ed., 101.
[2] *Ibid.*, 14.
[3] DANIEL TURNER, *The Ancient Physician's Legacy Impartially Survey'd*, 1733, Introduction, 3.

which is from Forty to Seventy grains. As monstrous as they may represent this, I can produce undeniable Proofs, where a Patient of mine has taken no less a Quantity than a Hundred grains, and yet has appeared abroad next Day. . . . This Notion of theirs proceeds entirely from their Ignorance, and from the Want of knowing the Nature of those Ingredients that are mix'd up with it, for they naturally weaken the Power of the Opium."[1]

Dover's powder is now exhibited as a diaphoretic, whereas he first used it as an analgesic in the excruciatingly painful condition of gout. Thus, in order to be effective, a much higher dose than is at present recommended would need to be administered. It is evident that Dover's original powder brought rapid relief. " In two or three hours, at farthest," he writes, " the patient will be perfectly free from Pain ; and though before not able to put one Foot to the ground, 'tis very much if he cannot walk the next Day. When it is taken, keep your Bed till next Day Noon. This remedy may be taken once a Week or once a Month."[2] It will be recalled that Sydenham suffered from gout, and when Dover refutes his critics (who accused him of being opposed to the use of opiates) he pays respectful homage to his former teacher. " I would not have the Reader imagine that I am an Enemy of Opiates ; I only look upon a constant and uninterrupted use of them to be pernicious. As I cannot fail of having the greatest Veneration for the Memory of my old Master Dr. Sydenham, I often remember his Observations, especially upon Opiates, which is as follows :—' Sine Papaveribus, sine opiates, et medicenantis ex vis confectis, manca et clauda esset Medicina'."[3]

The other ingredient of Dover's powder, ipecacuanha, was brought from Brazil by a Portuguese friar, and was first given for the " bloody flux ". In 1686 Helvetius used it successfully in France for the treatment of dysentery, and from him this secret remedy was bought by Louis XIV.[4] In

---

[1] THOMAS DOVER, *The Ancient Physician's Legacy*, 1742, 6th ed., 15.

[2] *Ibid.*, 14.

[3] *Ibid.*, 16.

[4] A. C. WOOTTON, *Chronicles of Pharmacy*, 1910, Vol. II, 114.

England it was favoured by Sir Hans Sloane, and Dover may have first noted its efficacy during his travels in South America or the West Indies.

After its introduction in 1732, Dover's powder was appropriated by the notorious quack, Joshua Ward (1685–1761), who popularized its use as a sweating powder. Shortly after Ward's death his book of secret remedies was published. Amongst many prescriptions appropriated from other sources, the book contained two powders, one identical with Dover's recipe, and the other, Dover's powder with the addition of white hellebore. This misappropriation probably saved the powder from obscurity, as it was from Ward's book of recipes that Dover's powder was first included in the 6th edition of the London Pharmacopœia published in 1788, forty-six years after its originator's death. Thus through successive pharmacopœias this emblem of sleep and gentle perspiration has come to take an humble place in an age of antibiotics and chemotherapy.

But Thomas Dover firmly believed that his permanent legacy to his country would not be his powder, but the use of quicksilver, which he stoutly recommended throughout the whole of his book. It was by means of *The Ancient Physician's Legacy* that his views on the medicinal properties of crude mercury became widely known, and eventually earned him the title of the " Quicksilver Doctor ".

CHAPTER XIV

THE QUICKSILVER DOCTOR

This is the way physicians mend or end us,
Secundum artem ; but although we sneer
In health—when ill, we call them to attend us,
Without the least propensity to jeer.

BYRON

THOMAS DOVER first used crude mercury in the treatment of
hysteria during his early years in Bristol. His book further
popularized his views, so that the use of quicksilver became the
main feature of his London practice. He prescribed it in the
treatment of intestinal infestation, scrofula, infertility, asthma,
syphilis, elephantiasis, scorbutic ulcers, intestinal obstruction,
and also for appendicitis, of which he says : " You need go no
further for the cure of this fatal disease than take a pound, or a
pound and a half of crude mercury ; and the late Queen
Caroline had but taken the same remedy, I will avow she
would have been well in twelve hours."[1]

His contemporaries dubbed him " the quicksilver doctor " ;
a well-earned title in which he gloried. " I desire to know
why I am called the quicksilver doctor by way of derision ? "
he asks, " Pray do not you gentlemen, physicians, surgeons
and apothecaries prescribe it almost every day of your lives ?
I avow you do ; only you disguise it, and I give it in such
an open honest manner that my patient cannot be deceived in
taking it. Let me ask you what is your Aethiops Mineral ?
Is it not quicksilver ground to a black powder with brimstone
and in as great esteem with you as any of your medicines ? A
very ingenious physician says, ' This is like striking a man
with your sword in a scabbard '."[2]

---

[1] THOMAS DOVER, *The Ancient Physician's Legacy*, 1742, 6th ed., 138.
[2] *Ibid.*, 75.

Dover gave quicksilver for three reasons. "First, it secures the patient from all vermicular diseases, of which no practitioner can be sufficiently apprised, who has not spent some time in hot climates. Next it opens all obstructions which are supposed to be another general cause of all diseases. Lastly, it makes a pure balsaam of the blood, beyond all other things in Creation. Otherwise why cannot venereal ulcers be cured without it ?   We often see those sores in a salivation grow well without the help of a surgeon."[1]

In support of his views Dover quotes the authority of three eminent medical men. Belloste, author of the *Hospital Surgeon*, refers to mercury as " the miracle of nature and the greatest gift of God in the whole of Materia Medica " ;[2] Dr. Freind, in his *Emmenologia*, states that quicksilver "not only opens obstructed vessels, but also blunts the points of acid " ;[3] and George Cheyne recommends Aethiops Mineral (mercury and sulphur) for cases of scorbutic and scrofulous ulcers, and rheumatism. Also letters from grateful patients were inserted in Dover's book testifying to the benefits of quicksilver in such varied complaints as " generalized pains ", asthma, " scorbutal humours ", and gout. But the most preposterous claim for the benefits of quicksilver was in a case of infertility, and is mentioned in a " letter from Russia ", which seems to indicate that Dover was deliberately pandering to the credulous :—

At Yamburg near Narva, one of the workmen of the glass houses there under my direction had been married twelve years without having had any children, at which time having by accident spilt a quantity of mercury, which he had brought to silver looking-glasses, among his house provisions, which he had brought at the same time, and put into the same bag ; he ate the said provisions so mixed with the mercury and reckoning from that time, his wife bore him a son, which son, has been both by the father and mother, and likewise of all their acquaintance, esteemed to have proceeded from the operation of the mercury, was commonly called by the nature of Artute the name of mercury in the Russian language.

(Signed) Samuel Jenkins.[4]

---

[1] THOMAS DOVER, *The Ancient Physician's Legacy*, 1742, 6th ed., 75.

[2] A. BELLOSTE, *Hospital Surgeon*, 1695, reprinted in 3rd ed. of *Ancient Physician's Legacy*, 1733, 10.

[3] J. FREIND, *Emmenologia*, 1703, 26.

[4] THOMAS DOVER, *The Ancient Physician's Legacy*, 1742, 6th ed., 70.

Dover firmly believed that quicksilver was a harmless medicine provided impurities (particularly lead) were first removed. He explains that injury results from taking drugs with " spiculæ, points, or edges ", whereas " quicksilver always retains a globular figure ". Prior to use, Dover recommended the following method of preparation. " I would advise the patient, that he get a small crucible, put into it the quantity of a pistol bullet of quicksilver, set the crucible on the fire, if any of the soft metals are put to it, they will remain, and the quicksilver will fly off. Note, a pound of lead costs two pence, and a pound of quicksilver eight or ten shillings. The profit that accrues may be one cause of its adulteration, and another to bring the medicine into disrepute."[1]

Metallic mercury was regarded with disfavour by the majority of eminent physicians, but these dignitaries of the College of Physicians did not escape Dover's rasping tongue and aggressive personality. Of them he says : " 'Tis a generally received notion, nay even among many Gentlemen of the Faculty, that quicksilver is a poison. If such persons are not ashamed of their being no better natural philosophers, I have no reason to be under confusion if faced with them. Their opinion is a sign that they have travelled far at home."[2] But Dover's boundless confidence in the efficacy of metallic mercury, together with his belligerent attitude, led other doctors to discredit his practice by attributing the death of a well-known actor, Barton Booth, to mercury poisoning following Dover's treatment.

In 1727, when at the peak of his career as a tragedian, Booth was seized with a fever which lasted for forty-six days. He returned to the stage again in the following spring, but shortly afterwards suffered a relapse, and became jaundiced. From then until his death six years later, Booth was a chronic invalid in vain pursuit of health. He had been impressed by the strong advocacy of quicksilver contained in *The Ancient Physician's Legacy*, and fearing a

[1] THOMAS DOVER, *The Ancient Physician's Legacy*, 1742, 6th ed., 85.
[2] *Ibid.*, 74.

return of his fever sent for Thomas Dover. According to Dr. Turner, who published the case as a postscript to his critical survey of *The Ancient Physician's Legacy*, Dover prescribed quicksilver, adding that it would not only prevent the return of his fever, " but would also effectually cure him of all his complaints ".[1]

This prediction proved to be tragically true, as Barton Booth died a week later after taking almost two pounds of quicksilver. Sir Hans Sloane, who had been called in two days before his death, had forbidden further oral quicksilver, and instead bled the patient to relieve his headache. At a post-mortem examination carried out by Mr. Small, surgeon, in the presence of Sir Hans Sloane, numerous stones were found in the gall-bladder and common bile duct. One stone, which was the size and shape of a " horse Bean, stopped bile from pouring into the duodenum " ; the intestines were black and lined with crude mercury ; and when the surgeon tried to divide the rectum, it was so rotten and blackened with mercury that " it broke between my fingers like tinder, and sent forth a most offensive cadaverous stench ".[2]

Turner's account of Barton Booth's death was hotly disputed in subsequent pamphlets. Physicians who believed that crude mercury was a poison quoted the tragic case of this well-known actor as an example of the danger of taking it. Another writer, " Mercurialist ",[3] contradicted Turner's account on the grounds that when mercury " destroys " a patient the intestines are always glazed, which was not evident in the case of Mr. Booth. Other pamphleteers favoured Turner's view, and denounced the use of metallic mercury in the strongest terms. Thus Dover's book, his increasing advocacy of crude mercury, and the death of Barton Booth, all provided material for a pamphlet war on the medicinal value of oral mercury which lasted for almost fifty years.

Dover's views on the use of quicksilver were stoutly upheld in a pamphlet called *Encomium Argenti Vivi*, by " a

---

[1], [2] DANIEL TURNER, *The Case of Mr. Booth*, included in *Ancient Physician's Legacy impartially Survey'd*, 1733, 269.

[3] " Mercurialist ", *A Short Review of the Quicksilver Controversy*, 1733, 2.

Gentleman of Trinity College, Cambridge ".[1] The author, after mentioning the principal European deposits of quicksilver, goes on to survey its chemical and physical properties. Of its current popularity he says that it is " as usual to meet with it in Families as snuff or tobacco ".[2]

After stating that the therapeutic action of crude mercury was to " cleanse the blood ", and " blunt the acids ", the author recommends its use for treating " the Pox, the Piles, scorbutic and scrophulous ulcers ; inflammations and fluxions of the Eyes, the Itch, the Leprosy, and all Cutaneous Foulnesses ; internal ulcers, rheumatisms, White Swellings, Tumours, sharp Humours in the stomach and guts ; stone, gout and Gravel ".[3] This gentleman from Trinity College sustained his treatise by quotations from the works of Belloste, Freind, and Cheyne, all of whom favoured the extensive use of mercury ; and of Dover he says :—

This gentleman hath been a practitioner for several years, and hath had several advantages which others have not had of observing the different methods of curing in different countries, as well as the different diseases which infest human nature ; from which a wise man may draw many useful conclusions. His book shows him to be both an honest and understanding man and is wrote with a very commendable design. He continues on the small practice prescribing quicksilver in a variety of cases, whilst the lazy, the Ignorant and the Unskillful are contented with jogging on in the old manner, and abusing those who study, at the smallest expense and with the least disgust, to relieve Mankind.[4]

Other writers were less kind to Dr. Dover. In a postscript to his pamphlet Mr. Bradley mentions deaths from poisoning and violent purging following quicksilver treatment. In a long discourse on quicksilver Dr. Turner states that he never prescribes the drug because of its toxicity and the fact that it is not absorbed when taken orally. He therefore condemns the boldness of Dover's practice, and his indiscriminate use of quicksilver. Turner illuminates his treatise with many crudely humorous accounts of the non-absorption of quicksilver, of which the following anecdote is an example. " I have heard a pleasant story of a mercurial lady, who in Dancing at a

[1,2] Gentleman of Trinity College, *Encomium Argenti Vivi*, 1733, 1.
[3] *Ibid.*, 36.
[4] *Ibid.*, 31.

Public Assembly, happened to let go some particles of the
quicksilver she had taken in the morning ; which, shining on
the floor in the midst of so great an illumination like so many
brilliants, there were several stooping down to take them up ;
but finding themselves deceived, it affected matter for much
laughter among the gentlemen, and blushing amongst the
ladies, especially she that was most concerned ; for the cry
went through the room, that some lady had scattered her
diamonds."[1]   Dr. Turner also mentions the case of a patient
who had taken sixteen pounds of crude mercury, collected
from his fæces only one and a half ounces short of the original
amount, which had probably been lost in the process of
separation ; thus, he concludes, " it is doubtless the case of
many, who thinking the remedy is working miracles in the
blood might find it in their breeches ".[2]

One of the least abusive and most scholarly criticisms of
Dover is contained in *A Treatise on Mercury . . . with some
remarks on the " Ancient Physician's Legacy "*, published
anonymously in 1733. When reviewing the past literature
on quicksilver the author refers to Giris's *Mercurius Triumphater*
wherein it is stated that workers in the mercury mines were
prone to generalized weakness, shaking palsy, and increasing
dyspnœa, so that even the strongest rarely survived in that
occupation for more than four years. He criticizes Dover for
failing to explain the therapeutic effects of crude mercury, and
for ignoring the dangers associated with its use. In the treatment
of kidney stone (for which condition Dover recommended
one ounce of quicksilver every morning) the anonymous
author suggests that, as the mercury is not excreted in
the urine, then no possible benefit can result from taking it.

Finally he summarizes the opinion of the majority of
London physicians, who agree that quicksilver is only of
value in the treatment of asthma, and that Dover's indiscriminate use of crude mercury can only benefit nurses and grave-
diggers. This pamphlet went into four editions as the
controversy became more heated, and in later accounts the

[1] DANIEL TURNER, *The Ancient Physician's Legacy Impartially Survey'd*,
1733, 144–145.
[2] *Ibid.*, 144.

author mentions many instances of the toxic effects of quicksilver. He does not even favour using crude mercury in the treatment of syphilis, as this thinly veiled libellous account shows :—" A young gentleman, son of Sir W – – – –, had the Venereal Disease, and, by fast living, his Constitution was so much impaired, that the regular Practitioners thought to Schust him. But Dr. D – – – – ordered the young gentleman to take crude mercury. At first he improved but later the patient had a violent dysentery which made an end to all his complaints, and his life also : To the great disappointment of all parties."[1]

However other writers who were not opposed to the use of quicksilver sprang to Dover's defence. Many of his critics were answered in a pamphlet by " Mercurialist "[2] called *A Short Review of the Quicksilver Controversy in a Letter to Dr. Dover.* The writer carefully avoids discussing either the action of quicksilver or its medicinal value : instead he confines his attention to praising Dover and his supporters, and abusing his critics. After thanking Dover for introducing " that good, grand Remedy Quicksilver ",[3] he praises Belloste and the author of *Encomium*, and dismisses Bradley's book of which he says, " I think his attempt personal, and may therefore be left to enjoy with Quacks a Place in some Apothecary's Library ".[4] The pamphlet is of only slight medical value as much of it is merely abusive. Of Dover's critics he writes, " The principal of them I take to be Dr. Turner : He follows the example of his friend Bradley who delighted himself in the witty conceit of calling you Captain, and bantering your Martial Exploits ; But notwithstanding these wags, it will not surely hurt your Character to be literally Tâm Marte quam Mercurio. The surgeon only let go a piece of wit, which was like to have burst him : But the Doctor vents his spleen when he represents your expedition into the South-Seas in quest of your countries Enemies in the odious light of a Pyrate."[5]

---

[1] ANON. *A Treatise on Mercury with some Remarks on the " Ancient Physician's Legacy,"* 1733, 31.
[2] " Mercurialist", *A Short Review of the Quicksilver Controversy*, 1733, 6.
[3] *Ibid.*, 9.
[4] *Ibid.*, 2.
[5] *Ibid.*, 10.

In each edition of his *Legacy* Dover includes more letters from patients who had benefited from taking quicksilver and he also continues to answer his detractors. One of them (also anonymous) in his treatise *On the Use and Abuse of Mercury* (1733), describes it as a " slow poison ";[1] later he chides Dover for failing to explain its exact mode of action, and is particularly severe on him for prescribing crude mercury in cases of renal calculi. Dover replied to these criticisms in a small pamphlet which first appeared at the end of the fourth edition of his book. " I have taken it myself above six and forty years ", he writes. " I have been in all sorts of climates ; and am now upwards of seventy ; and yet, I thank God, enjoy a perfect state of Health : If I should happen to die twenty or thirty years hence, this author may, if he pleases, impute my Death to this slow way of poisoning."[2]

When answering the other criticisms Dover shows less assurance ; he refuses to be drawn into explaining the pharmacological action of crude mercury, and is content to affirm that quicksilver does " wonders in the stone ".[3] Finally he shoots off at a tangent with a vigorous onslaught on the methods of other physicians. He mentions a recent visit to a child who had previously been treated by four eminent physicians. The baby had been " twice vomited, twice blooded, an Issac cut in his Neck ; his Head, his Back, his Arms, his Thighs, his Legs, the Soles of his Feet, all blistered in four days Time, when it pleas'd God by Death to take him out of the Hands of his Tormentors ".[4]

The paper war continued. Another pamphlet in which the virtues of quicksilver are loudly acclaimed was first published separately in 1733, and later in the same year was included in the fourth edition of *The Ancient Physician's Legacy*. It was probably written by Dover and bears the whimsical title :— *Substantial Reasons offer'd by Way of Argument to prove that crude mercury never did, nor can hurt any one taking it. Being*

---

[1] *On the Use and Abuse of Mercury*, by a Country Physician, 1733, 3.

[2] THOMAS DOVER, *To the Author of "The Use and Abuse of Mercury"*, *The Ancient Physician's Legacy*, 1733, 4th ed., 201.

[3] *Ibid.*, 205.

[4] *Ibid.*, 211.

the greatest Discovery that was ever made to Mankind. By Hydrargyrum of York. " Merry Andrew to the Antient Physician. Drawn up by the Author when he was broad awake but somewhat in a Transport."[1]

As the title suggests, this pamphlet lists ten reasons (most of them medically irrelevant) for using metallic mercury. For example, the first reason for its use is, " because Physicians are obstinately tenacious of their old general Rules, and treat every prying Reference as a Tryt, the want of Orthodoxy in Physick, being as unpardonable a Crime with them as is part of Doctrine with the Clergy ".[2] Indeed some of the arguments serve only to illustrate the abusive tenor of medical controversy, and to enable the author to score off his detractors. " Because a physical, philosophical Barber Surgeon has treated the Ancient Physician very roughly, and address'd himself to the Apothecaries in hopes of stepping into the college in his Neighbourhood " is an aspersion on Mr. Bradley.[3]

Other suggested reasons for giving mercury are because one of Dover's critics (Dr. Turner) " spends his many leisure Hours in the service of the Fraternity " ; and also because physicians " slay their Thousands and ten thousands yearly in a regular Course of Purging, Bleeding and Blistering ".[4]

A letter in *The Ancient Physician's Legacy* is also signed by " your true Friend Hydrargyrum " ; it is virtually a letter from Mercury extolling its own virtues. Addressed to Dr. Dover, who is upbraided for being so generous and benevolent towards an undeserving public, the writer directs a long diatribe against all his critics. He says that Dover has been labelled a " quack ", an " empiric ", and a " nostrum-monger ",[5] which are hardly familiar terms amongst men of real learning, but more common forms of address by the women of Billingsgate. Having himself failed to produce

---

[1] HYDRARGYRUM, " *Substantial Reasons Offer'd* . . . ", *The Ancient Physician's Legacy*, 1733, 4th ed.

[2] *Ibid.*, 1.

[3] *Ibid.*, 3.

[4] *Ibid.*, 5.

[5] THOMAS DOVER, *The Ancient Physician's Legacy*, 1742, 6th ed., 178. Letter from Hydrargyrum, York, May 4th, 1733.

any scientific reasons for using quicksilver, the author then invokes mercury to his aid, and concludes his letter in a haze of mysticism, such as Paracelsus and his cult of alchemists used :—

> My name you know, and Experience has shown you some of my Good Qualities ; but be not vainly inquisitive to know more of me ; for my Nature and Efficacy is Incomprehensible to human faculties, and will eternally deride the studious labours of the best curious Searchers into Mysteries. If you torture me of Fire, and Stop my Flight can I do less than resent such cruel Usage by gripping, rending, and in various ways exerting my just Rage on the first Object I am let loose to? Whereas unchanged by Art and in the pure State Providence offers me, I am truly a Friend to Mankind, affording Comfort and Relief to the most Miserable, who will have as much faith and confidence in me, as they have blindly reposed in many varieties of poisons.[1]

The Antidote was the name of another pamphlet supporting Dover's views, which added nothing to the previous arguments. It was followed in 1737 by a critical treatise called *Remarks upon a Late Scurilous Pamphlet Entitled " A Review of the Quicksilver Controversy ", in which Dr. Turner's Character as a Great and Impartial Historian in Regard to the Same is granted, and the Author's own Impartiality, Sincerity, Falsehood and Gross Ignorance are Set Forth*, by a Country Physician.[2] As can be expected from the title, this pamphlet made no medical contribution to the controversy : the author resurrects the case of Barton Booth whose death he ascribes to metallic mercury, and when addressing " Mercurialist ", says " the man is mad, and so must be his Patron (Dover) to whom this Ribaldry is addressed ".[3]

Immediately following Dover's book, I have traced fourteen other books or pamphlets treating the medicinal aspect of metallic mercury ; there may have been many more as it was a topic of some importance to the eighteenth-century practitioner. Yet a review of these works, whilst reflecting the spirit of medical polemics, also demonstrates a complete disregard for reasonable clinical inquiry. Only one physician,

---

[1] THOMAS DOVER, *The Ancient Physician's Legacy*, 1742, 6th ed., 181.

[2] COUNTRY PHYSICIAN, *Remarks upon a Late Scurilous Pamphlet Entitled "A Review of the Quicksilver Controversy"*, etc., 1737.

[3] *Ibid.*, 27.

Boerhaave, contributed a work of scientific value to this controversy. In his treatise *Some Experiments concerning Mercury*, published in 1734, he confines his attention to reporting the physical and chemical properties of mercury as he observed in a series of experiments. By strongly heating metallic mercury, he obtained a black powder, and after further heating he again obtained pure mercury. As a result of this, and other experiments, he postulated that mercury was an element which could not be split into other metals.[1]

However, the " Quicksilver Doctor " practised his art unperturbed by the pamphlets of his detractors. Judging by later editions of his book, he came to use metallic mercury on an increasing scale. But Dover was promoting nothing new by urging the use of mercury, which in one form or another is probably one of the oldest remedies. It is said to have been used in 2637 B.C. by the Chinese Emperor Hoang-Ty ; and Arabian physicians favoured the external application of mercurial ointments before its medicinal properties were first described in Europe by Matthaeus Plateurius in A.D. 1140. Throughout the fifteenth and sixteenth centuries mercury was widely used in Europe, particularly for the treatment of syphilis, which disease had reached alarming proportions. It derives its name from the poem *Syphilis sive morbus Gallicus* published at Verona in 1530. The poet, who is determined to " seek the secret causes in the profound mystery of the air and the stellar spaces", mentions mercury and guaiacum as specifics in this fell disease.[2]

At that time the mode of administration was either by fumigation or in the form of an unction. During the sixteenth century Paracelsus and his fellow alchemists popularized the use of mercury in all its forms, and following the publication of his *Manual on Mercury in Syphilis* (1553), the drug became part of the pharmacopœia. Fracastorius also strongly upheld its use against many prejudices, but throughout the centuries mercury, in common with many other drugs, has suffered the fluctuation of therapeutic favour.

---

[1] H. BOERHAAVE, *Some Experiments concerning Mercury*, 1734, 10.
[2] A. CASTIGLIONI, *A History of Medicine*, 1947, 459.

Before Dover's time the salts of mercury, made into unctions for external application, had found more favour than oral treatment with the pure metal. But quicksilver had been used by Paracelsus; later (as mentioned by Dover), it was favoured by Sir Nicholas Butler during the reign of James II; and again, Belloste in France had used metallic mercury extensively during the early part of the eighteenth century. It can, therefore, be concluded that Thomas Dover merely popularized metallic mercury as a medicine at a time when it had lost favour.

With the present knowledge of therapeutics, there seems little doubt that Dover's heroic doses of oral quicksilver were only *psychologically* effective; though particularly useful in such conditions as asthma when even his critics realized its value. Metallic mercury given orally is not absorbed from the alimentary tract but is harmlessly excreted.

Before the development of abdominal surgery, metallic mercury was given without ill effect in single one-pound doses in order to relieve intestinal obstruction. But compounds of mercury are toxic, the degree of which is related to the rate of ionization of the mercuric ion. However, prolonged oral administration of quicksilver, although unabsorbed from the alimentary tract, could have produced toxic symptoms, either by inhalation of its vapour (as Dover recommended heating before use) or by frequent contact with the metal, and thereby allowing free absorption through the skin. Dover had been taking oral quicksilver himself for forty-six years, with no ill effects, although it is interesting to note that all specimens of his handwriting show a noticeable tremor—probably constitutional.

However, Thomas Dover tenaciously voiced his views on the medicinal properties of metallic mercury, even when his own observations suggested that in such a form the metal could not be absorbed and was virtually inert. In the sixth edition of his book, published in the year of his death, he actually describes a case of syphilis in which quicksilver had not been absorbed. "It suffices to my present purpose", he writes, "to have proved that pure mercury is not poisonous or corrosive; and therefore, not only have I seen two ounces of it given every day, for one and twenty days together, without any inconvenience at all; but found once some Quantity of it in the Perineum of a Subject I took from the Gallows for a Dissection (whose rotten bones quickly discovered what disease it was had required the Use of it, and that, I suppose, chiefly in External Application by Unction), without any mark of corrosion of the part where it was lodged."[1]

But although the later years of Dover's practice were marred by constantly vaunting the use of quicksilver in a far too rash and forceful manner, this aspect of his career brought him fame in the metropolis and a minor continental reputation, and the " Quicksilver Doctor " received high praise in an eleven-page preface to the *Opera Omnia Medici* of Ballonius.[2]

---

[1] THOMAS DOVER, *The Ancient Physician's Legacy*, 1742, 6th ed., 84.
[2] BALLONIUS, *Opera Omnia Medici*, 1734–6, 1.

CHAPTER XV

DR. DOVER AND HIS CRITICS

From Earth's dark centre unto Saturn's Gate
I've Solved all problems of this World's Estate,
From every snare of Plot and Guile set free,
Each bond resolved, saving alone Death's Fate.

AVICENNA[1]

IT would appear that Thomas Dover's varying fortunes had
revived once more following the stimulus of his *Legacy*, for
in 1736, four years after its publication, he moved westwards
to Arundel Street, but still continued to meet his apothecary
at the Jerusalem Coffee House in the Strand. His martial
exploits, his quicksilver treatment, and his book with its
flavour of self-advertisement, all added, for good or ill, to his
reputation. But although Dr. Dover was a well-known
physician it is unlikely that he ever gained the popularity or
respect of his professional colleagues. Modesty was not one
of his virtues.

Dover's arrogance is particularly evident when recounting
the details of patients he had cured, despite the fact that
their illness had previously baffled less gifted physicians.
Perhaps Dr. Mounsey[2] had such incidents in mind when,
following a quarrel with David Garrick, he wrote these
satirical verses, which were later suppressed on Garrick's
death :—

> Seven wise physicians lately met
> To serve a wretched sinner ;
> Come Tom, says Jack, pray let's be quick,
> Or I shall lose my dinner.

---

[1] 980–1038. Persian poet and physician. MSS. in Bodleian Library.
[2] F. B. WINSLOW, *Physic and Physicians*, 1842, Vol. I, 52.

After the consultation there seems to have been some disagreement amongst the physicians, as :—

> Some roar'd for rhubarb, julop some,
> And some cried out for Dover.
> Let's give him something each man said,
> Why e'en let's give him—over.

Dover's overbearing conceit, so noticeable in his writing, tends to hinder a serious and objective assessment of his true ability. Indeed, many extravagances in *The Ancient Physician's Legacy* seem to be the work of a poseur ; writing occasionally with tongue in cheek, but invariably with the object of provoking criticism. Yet once these bombastic sallies are regarded as defects of character, rather than of medicine, then a review of the purely medical material in his book (whether accurate or otherwise) does at least bear the stamp of sincerity. There is no evidence to suggest that his treatment was merely designed to gain popular favour. On the contrary Dover's sincerity in refusing to vary his prescriptions earned the apothecaries' displeasure, and thereby adversely affected his practice. But some of his self acclamations appear to be too histrionic, too ridiculous, and too strident for the utterances of a self deceiver. It is perhaps these conflicting considerations which have led medical men to form widely different conclusions when judging his worth as a physician.

Sir Norman Moore[1] considers that the standard of medicine displayed in Dover's book is low ; and that it sold only amongst the uninformed who believed in its profession of giving " the power of art without the show ". Similar views have been more strongly expressed by other doctors, who have variously dismissed him as a " mountebank ", " quack ", and " buccaneer ". But some medical writers take the opposite view. They regard Thomas Dover as a sound practical physician, and praise his powder, his understanding of the nature of various diseases, his endeavours to rid medicine of many time-worn nostrums, and above all they applaud his energy, initiative, and determination. Sir William Osler[2]

---

[1] SIR NORMAN MOORE, *Dictionary of National Biography*, 1909, Vol. V, 1286.

[2] SIR WILLIAM OSLER, *Johns Hopk. Hosp. Bull.*, 1890, **7**, 4.

takes the *via media* : whilst remarking on Dover's too scanty descriptions of disease, he applauds his honesty of purpose—particularly in his dealings with apothecaries.

But as these views are based only on interpretations of Dover's *Legacy*, together with Rogers's biased account of his behaviour during their voyage, they are all somewhat limited conclusions, as they fail to take cognizance of his life as a whole. It is quite evident that Dover's training, followed as it was by long and varied experience, afforded him, in ample measure, the opportunity of developing into an outstanding physician. But certain traits of character thwarted the promise of his early years. Even when due allowance is made for Rogers's harsh views, and Dover's period as a London physician is also viewed in the most charitable light, one is still forced to conclude that he was an arrogant and cantankerous man. Impatient of authority, he had an independent mind with the courage to voice his convictions which he continued to uphold tenaciously in spite of all opposition, and often with a complete disregard for conflicting evidence. Such a temperament would obviously tend to mar his potentialities as a physician.

Yet Dover must be credited with initiative, determination, and charity towards the poor ; and, when well advanced in years, he was still receptive to new ideas. His treatment of small-pox and other fevers was highly regarded ; his impatience with time-worn remedies was commendable ; his early advocacy of inoculation, his powder, his excellent results in the treatment of the plague, and his integrity in relations with the apothecaries, all indicate the competent physician.

But his most obvious failing was a lack of moderation. This characteristic is most evident in his use of quicksilver. Though perhaps the best eighteenth-century remedy, when limited to the treatment of intestinal obstruction and certain psychological disorders, it was of no benefit whatsoever when administered indiscriminately. He was also inclined to bleed patients to an extreme degree. Likewise Dover's prejudices were carried to immoderate limits. His opposition to blistering in small-pox is highly commendable, but he goes too far in condemning its use in other conditions. Also his

PLATE IX

A

R E P L Y

TO THE

R E M A R K S

ON THE

TREATISE of the Use and Abuse of Mercury, in Dr. *Dover's Antient Physician's Legacy*, Edit. IV.

SIR,

THE Title of the fourth Edition of your *Antient Physician's Legacy*, gave me great Hopes you wou'd, by Dint of Reasoning, prove my Objections to be weak, or that my Consequences are not fairly drawn

First page of *A Reply to the Remarks on the Treatise of the Use and Abuse of Mercury*, in Dr. Dover's "Ancient Physician's Legacy", 4th edition, 1733.

(*Wellcome Historical Medical Library.*)

THE

ANCIENT PHYSICIAN's LEGACY impartially survey'd;

And his PRACTICE prov'd Repugnant, not only to that of the best antient and modern Physicians, but to the very Nature of those Diseases (many of them) of which he undertakes to give us an Account; inconsistent even with those very Indications himself at some Times lays down for the Cure.

WITH

Practical OBSERVATIONS upon each Chapter.

IN

A LETTER *to a Country Physician.*
To which is added,

In the way of POSTSCRIPT,

A Discourse on *Quicksilver,*
As now commonly Taken:
And the good or bad Effects which have thence ensued.

AS ALSO,

A particular Account of Monsieur *Belloft's* Pill compar'd with the Author's.
And the CASE of *Barton Booth,* Esq;
the late famous *Tragedian,*
As the same was communicated to the Author by Mr. *Alexander Small,* Surgeon,
who open'd the Body in the Presence of Sir *Hans Sloan.*

By DANIEL TURNER,
of the College of Physicians, London.

London, *Printed for John Clarke, at the Bible under the* Royal Exchange, Cornhill. 1733;

Title-page of *The Ancient Physician's Legacy impartially survey'd*, by Daniel Turner, 1733.

PLATE X

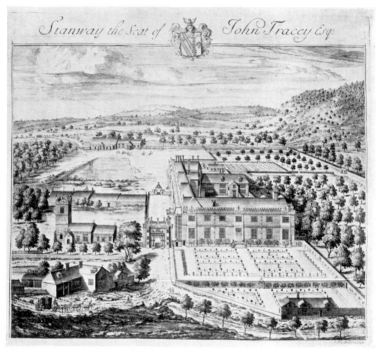

Stanway House, Gloucestershire.   Thomas Dover's last residence.
(*Bodleian Library.*)

Stanway House, gateway.

Stanway House, gatehouse and forecourt.

(By courtesy of "Country Life".)

PLATE XII

Stanway Church.

onslaughts against the College of Physicians reached a wholly unjustified tempo of vituperation.

Unfortunately only slight information can be gleaned from contemporary sources. It is known that he was on friendly though respectful terms with Sir Hans Sloane, who occasionally entrusted patients to his care. However, his main critic was Dr. Turner, formerly a surgeon, but later admitted a Licentiate of the College of Physicians. He practised in Devonshire Square and seems to have gained some reputation as a dermatologist, for he was the originator of ceratum calamine, which was linked with his name in several editions of the *London Pharmacopœia*. Turner is also said to have been fond of displaying his talents on paper, which resulted in many books, which were rapidly forgotten. Often Dr. Turner's views were not presented in the most delicate terms; nor was politeness one of his characteristics. His detailed and sweeping criticisms are too biased to be of any real value in judging Dover's worth.

Dover's other antagonist, Bradley, a surgeon whose book was dedicated to the Company of Apothecaries, was even more abusive, and therefore cannot be taken seriously. For example when commenting on Dover's treatment of rheumatism, Bradley writes: " I am much surpris'd that he should conceal one Nostrum (which I'm inform'd he puts a greater Confidence in, for the Cure of this Disease than any other) which is, hot broiled Beef-Stakes well butter'd apply'd to the affected Parts; which may have this one sensible and good Effect, that if it don't cure the Patient, will make the Doctor a good dinner."[1]

There were no notable changes during the final years of Thomas Dover's practice. Judging from later editions of his book, his declining years were merely an extension of earlier trends; quicksilver was more frequently exhibited, and he intensified his private campaign against the College of Physicians. Each edition of his book contains more letters from grateful patients, and at the same time refutes the

---

[1] H. BRADLEY, *Physical and Philosophical Remarks on Dr. Dover's Late Pamphlet*, 1733, 45.

allegations of his critics, as in the case of John Dinely Goodere, of whom the statement " some people maliciously reported that instead of the most violent Fever that I ever saw, labour'd only under a Fit of Drunkenness ",[1] was contradicted by a letter from the patient's father, Sir Edward Goodere.

Dr. Turner sweepingly dismissed *The Ancient Physician's Legacy* as " absurd " and " Romantick ", serving only " to amuse the Ignorant, for whom doubtless it was intended ; as it can never pass with Men of any tolerable Judgment in Physick, or surely, one might imagine of Common Understanding ".[2] But Dover was well capable of answering his critics in terms no less scathing. He describes Dr. Turner as " a Barber Surgeon turn'd into a Doctor, in grateful Remembrance of such his Advancement, employs his many leisure Hours in Service of the Fraternity ".[3]

Mr. Bradley's motives in dedicating his book to the Company of Apothecaries he regards as " a piece of Policy absolutely necessary in Young Practitioners, and not to be totally Neglected by the most venerable Sages of the Profession ; for whose Reputation can long stand the Shock of a Universal charge rung upon their melodious Mortars? "[4]

In the sixth edition of his *Legacy*, published in 1742, Dover includes his views on midwifery in a short appendix. He begins in a sanctimonious manner : " 'Tis true, the woman that transgress'd in eating the Forbidden Fruit, the Curse laid on her, in Sorrow she shall conceive and bring forth Children, and her Husband shall rule over her ; which, I humbly conceive, all the Families of the Brutal Kind and others have been Sharers in. The Transgression of the Man in eating the Forbidden Fruit, descended to the whole Earth, which should bring forth nothing but ' briars and thorns, without the Sweat of his Brow ' ; thus we see almost the whole creation suffer by their Transgression ; ' the Serpent was cursed of all Cattle,

---

[1] THOMAS DOVER, *The Ancient Physician's Legacy*, 1742, 6th ed., 146.
[2] DANIEL TURNER, *The Ancient Physician's Legacy Impartially Survey'd*, 1733, 129.
[3] THOMAS DOVER, *The Ancient Physician's Legacy*, 1742, 6th ed., 178.
[4] *Ibid.*

on his Belly he should go, and eat dust all the days of his life'."[1]

His advice is brief, simple, and sound. During the early stages of pregnancy Dover recommends a natural way of living with a light diet with plenty of rest and moderate exercise. He deplores the habit (particularly common amongst wealthy women) of taking to their beds early in pregnancy for fear of a miscarriage. Dover also warns midwives against the common practice of bringing about a delivery too precipitately : afterwards he strongly recommends breast feeding. " The Mother gives Milk to the Fruit of her own Body, being the most Natural ; if her Constitution will not bear it, the Excuse is very warrantable, and more else but our delicate fine Ladies must not by nursing spoil their Breasts, but how often does Judgment follow them by Milk sores in their Breasts, and by that fulsome way of plaistering, and repelling the Milk, bring on the Milky Fever, which carries off many of them. The remedy I would prescribe to help such miserable creatures, is to wet a large quantity of cotton in strong Spirits and wear in under their Armpits for a fortnight or Three weeks which will draw off the serum of the Blood."[2]

In his treatise on midwifery, Dover mentions a curious incident which occurred when he was called to a merchant's house near the " dead time of the night ".[3] He was met by a girl who told him that, unknown to the rest of the family, her sister had given birth to a child, which was still lying under her. After getting the relatives out of the room, Dover pulled the child away, whereupon it cried out and began to breathe : thus he concluded that the reason the baby had not suffocated was because it had never previously drawn breath.

The mother never married, but reared the child, and eventually died with a most virtuous character. This anecdote was intended to show that midwives erred in bringing about

---

[1] THOMAS DOVER, *Essay on Midwifery* in *The Ancient Physician's Legacy*, 1742, 6th ed., 214.

[2] *Ibid.*, 217.

[3] *Ibid.*, 216.

precipitate births ; as this child had thrived in spite of making its way "into the World under so great a Disadvantage ". This essay on midwifery was written " out of the pure Regard and Love I have towards the Fair Sex ", and in so doing he says, " I have deviated something from my Profession ".[1]

Thomas Dover probably retired in 1741, the year before he trenchantly denounced the College of Physicians in the sixth edition of his *Legacy*. This renegade action takes the form of a critical commentary on their Statutes of Morality, copies of which are included in Latin and English. In the assumed role of medical reformer, Dover also criticizes their " Moral Conversations and Penal Statutes ",[2] which regulate the ethics of consultation, and lay down fines for their non-observance. Although a trifle cumbersome and pompous, these regulations were not unreasonable ; and Dover's accusations (one of which was that the physician must " first raise a Fever before he can cure it ")[3] seem wholly unjustified. The apothecaries and surgeons also reap his sarcastic comments, the latter because they invariably confirm the physician's diagnosis at post-mortems, as either a " Polypus in the Heart " or, what was then more fashionable, " Mortification of the Bowel . . . so that the great Art of Healing may for ever be established ".[4]

At this time Thomas Dover was over 80. Since his youth medical practice had become more highly organized, practitioners were more mercenary in their outlook, and co-operated in groups for their mutual benefit. As mentioned earlier, the profession was passing through one of its less creditable epochs, and these considerations most likely contributed to the contemptuous manner in which Dover frequently addressed himself to his professional colleagues. Another reason he gives for abusing the " Gentlemen of the Faculty " was because his enemies amongst them had constantly tried to discredit his practice. His final flourish

---

[1] Thomas Dover, *Essay on Midwifery* in *The Ancient Physician's Legacy*, 1742, 6th ed., 219.

[2] Thomas Dover, *Statutes of Morality Belonging to the College of Physicians*, *The Ancient Physician's Legacy*, 1742, 6th ed., 230.

[3], [4] *Ibid.*, 244.

against these detractors is not without a touch of truculent grandeur :—

I do not seek for Applause from this Performance, especially from the Gentlemen of the Faculty, being sensible how many powerful enemies I have amongst them. Who, as they have done all they could hitherto to discredit my practice, so probably will take occasion from the publication of these sheets, to prove their invectives and resentments against me. But as Custom has made ill Usage familiar to me, I think I am prepared for my future Calumny. In the meantime I would caution unwary people against one thing ; which is not to mistake every graduate for a physician, nor a clan of prejudiced gentlemen for Oracles. Experience is all in all ; and I will venture to say some Experience has fallen to my share having sought it in other places besides the shops of Apothecaries, or the College of Physicians.[1]

Thomas Dover spent the last few months of his life at Stanway Hall in his native Cotswolds. There he was better respected than in London, where as the dogmatic quicksilver doctor and hot tempered circumnavigator he had constantly vexed both physicians and apothecaries. He died in 1742, and was buried on April 27 in the vault of the Tracy family at Stanway Church.

Some 70 years ago, when this church was restored, a new altar was built over the vault, and obliterated his only memorial. This is less than his memory deserves : for although the swashbuckling exploits of Captain Dover, circumnavigator, self-acclaimed victor of Guayaquil, and the man who actually found Alexander Selkirk, are now forgotten, Dr. Dover has drifted into our modern life as the physician who had the wit to compound a powder which is still a household remedy. In spite of his faults, which were neither few nor small, " as he was a man of rough temper who could not easily agree with those about him " ;[2] yet at the same time he was a bluff, hearty, headstrong Englishman with some likeable qualities for whom the lines of Keats provide a fair and fitting epitaph :—

> Not the eagle more
> Loves to beat up against a tyrannous blast
> Than I to meet the torrent of my foes.
> This is a brag !—be it so ; but, if I fall,
> Carve it upon my scutcheon's sepulchre.

---

[1] THOMAS DOVER, *The Ancient Physician's Legacy*, 1742, 6th ed., 112.
[2] SIR WILLIAM OSLER, *Johns Hopk. Hosp. Bull.*, 1896, **7**, 6.

APPENDIX

DOVER, SELKIRK, DEFOE, AND THE ORIGIN OF ROBINSON CRUSOE

I am monarch of all I survey
My right there is none to dispute ;
From the centre all round to the Sea,
I am lord of the fowl and the brute.

COWPER

THE factual basis of Defoe's *Robinson Crusoe* has been a subject of perennial interest. There can be no doubt whatsoever that Thomas Dover actually rescued Alexander Selkirk from the island of Juan Fernandez, as two accounts bear witness to that event. Later, when Dover was appointed Commander of the *Batchelor*, Selkirk served as his sailing master, and in these roles they returned from the Californian coast (via the Dutch East Indies and the Cape of Good Hope) to England.

Selkirk's adventures attracted public interest at the time of his home-coming. Sir Richard Steele's account of his conversation with Selkirk in no way differs from Rogers's and Cooke's versions. " The person I speak of is Alexander Selkirk ", he says, " whose name is familiar to Men of Curiosity, from the Fame of his having lived four years and four months alone on the island of Juan Fernandez. I had the pleasure frequently to converse with the Man soon after his arrival in England in the year 1711." [1] So much is known to be true.

But the subsequent relations between author, mariner, and physician have been the subject of much speculation. It is popularly held in Bristol that Dover introduced Selkirk to

---

[1] SIR RICHARD STEELE, *The Englishman*, 1713, December, No. 26, 3.

Defoe in the Star Tavern. There, it is alleged that Selkirk was persuaded to part with the material concerning his adventures on Juan Fernandez to the famous author, who swelled his narrative into *Robinson Crusoe*. The truth of this story now depends on the accumulation of evidence from two questions : (*a*) Was *Robinson Crusoe* conceived on the factual basis of Selkirk's adventures, and his rescue by Dover ? (*b*) What evidence is there to suggest that Defoe met either Dover or Selkirk ?

The earliest writer who states that Selkirk's experiences provided the plot for *Robinson Crusoe* is Entick. In his *Naval History* (1757) he writes : " Mr. Selkirk, on his coming to England, supplied Daniel Defoe, who was pillory'd, with his Memoirs, in order to digest them for Publication ; but that honest Writer stole the Materials, which he gave to the Public under the Name of *Robinson Crusoe*." [1]

Dr. Beattie supports these views in his *Dissertations Moral and Critical* (1783), in which he writes :—

Selkirk was advised to get his story put in writing, and published. Being illiterate himself, he told everything he could remember to Daniel Defoe, a professed author of considerable note ; who, instead of doing justice to the poor man, is said to have applied these materials to his own use by making them the groundwork of *Robinson Crusoe* ; which he after published, and which, being very popular, brought him a good deal of money. I am willing to believe, that Defoe shared the profits of this publication with the poor seaman : for there is an air of humanity in it, which one would not expect from an author who is an arrant cheat.[2]

Similar views are expressed in a series of letters in the *Gentleman's Magazine*. The first writer (signing himself " Philobiblios ")[3] asks of the author of *Robinson Crusoe*, " Whence came so able a geographer ? Not only a geographer, but so well acquainted with the manners of savages, and with the productions animal and vegetable of America?" This letter is answered by " Subscriber "[4] who reaffirms the story that Selkirk handed his diary to Defoe for editing, but instead, the author swelled Selkirk's experiences

---

[1] John Entick, *A New Naval History*, 1757, 673.
[2] James Beattie, *Dissertations Moral and Critical*, 1783, 565.
[3] " Philobiblios ", *Gentleman's Magazine*, 1785, Vol. LV, 889.
[4] " Subscriber ", *Ibid.*, 1785, Vol. LV, 1895.

into *Robinson Crusoe*.   A third correspondent gives a detailed account of Selkirk's adventures, and also states that Defoe stole Selkirk's papers. "These papers", he writes, "must have been drawn up after he left Juan Fernandez, as he had no means of recording his transactions there."   The anonymous writer refers to Captain Cooke's account wherein it is stated that Selkirk recorded the date by cutting notches in a post, just as Defoe makes Robinson Crusoe do.   The writer infers that Defoe "very dishonestly defrauded the original proprietor of his share of the profits ".[1]

It is significant to note that none of these writers produces any evidence to sustain their accusations against Defoe.   The only one of Defoe's biographers to take this view is Thomas Wright, who states in his introduction that he is " able to settle once and for ever the vexed question as to whence Defoe obtained the bulk of the material upon which *Robinson Crusoe* is founded " ; and he continues, " I give a photograph of the house of Mrs. Daniells in Bristol where Defoe met Selkirk ".[2]   His evidence takes the form of an undated letter from H. C. Harford to the Editor of the *Bristol Mirror*. Harford writes that he had been informed by his grandfather, who in turn had been told by Mrs. Daniells, " that Selkirk had informed her that he had placed his papers in Defoe's hands ". This letter is followed by a document entitled, *Memoranda after a Conversation with W. P. Lunnell*, 5th August, 1834, which purports to give an account of their meeting :—

Mrs. Daniells lived at a corner house in James Square, Bristol.   Here she was visited by Alexander Selkirk, then recently returned from his solitary abode on the Island of Juan Fernandez. . . .   There also she was accustomed to entertain Daniel De Foe.   It was in her house that Selkirk gave De Foe an account of his adventures for which De Foe drew up a narrative of Selkirk which was published.   Many years later Defoe wrote and published his romance of *Robinson Crusoe*, the notion of which was suggested by Selkirk's narrative.[3]

This dubious account, supported only by indirect testimony, has been rejected by all Defoe's other biographers ; yet they

---

[1] *Gentleman's Magazine*, 1788, Vol. LX, 206.

[2] THOMAS WRIGHT, *The Life of Daniel Defoe*, 1894, 16.

[3] THOMAS WRIGHT, *Memoranda after a Conversation with W. P. Lunnell*, Appendix C, *Life of Daniel Defoe*, 1894.

agree that Selkirk's isolation on Juan Fernandez gave Defoe
the original idea of writing *Robinson Crusoe*. These authors
include D'Israeli (1817), Wilson (1830), Hazlitt (1840), the
author of an undated introduction to the Cassell Petten and
Galpin edition, Chadwick (1859), Whitten (1901), and
Maynadier (1903); who all agree that although *Robinson
Crusoe* is, in part, based on Selkirk's experiences, there is no
evidence to suggest that Defoe stole the mariner's papers.
All these writers consider that Defoe had easy access to all the
material relating to Selkirk's adventures in the published
works of Rogers, Cooke, and Steele, and therefore there was
no necessity, either to borrow Selkirk's papers, or indeed
even converse with him.

Austin Dobson believes that Defoe got the first idea of his
masterpiece from Steele's paper, whereas Whitley and
Maynadier are both of the opinion that Rogers's book was the
more likely source. Also Howell, in his life of Selkirk,
rightly asks: " What could he (Selkirk) say to De Foe that
he had not already told to all the others?"[1]

Aitken gives one of the most complete and balanced
summaries of this vexed question in his introduction to
Robinson Crusoe published in 1895 :—

Whether or no Defoe had himself seen Selkirk, one cannot say. There
is a tradition that Selkirk drew up a narrative of his adventures, which he
gave to Defoe to prepare for publication, and that Defoe made note of
the contents of the papers, and then informed Selkirk that they were
worthless, though he ultimately gave Selkirk half of the profits derived
from *Robinson Crusoe*. This tale has nothing to support it. Selkirk was
not a man likely to write a detailed account of his experiences ; and if
there had been papers, they would have been published long before 1714.
Defoe's enemies made no charge of plagiarism, and there can be no doubt
that Selkirk told all he had to say to Rogers and Steele. Mr. Wright has
recently stated that Defoe went to see Selkirk at Bristol ; that they met at
the house of Mrs. Daniells, and that Selkirk gave Defoe his papers. But
the documents upon which these statements are based are not very con-
vincing ; the story they tell had gone through a good many hands, and
it is not very consistent. In one place it is stated that Defoe published
Selkirk's narrative before the novel was written, but no such narrative is
known. Moreover, it was not necessary for Defoe to go to Bristol to see
Selkirk. I do not believe that Defoe would have learned anything from

---

[1] JOHN HOWELL, *The Life and Adventures of Alexander Selkirk*, 1829, 15.

12

Selkirk which is not in the accounts of Rogers, Cooke and Steele; and it seems not unreasonable to suppose that the story was recalled to Defoe's mind in 1718 by the second edition of *Rogers' Voyage*.[1]

Furthermore Wright's allegations of plagiarism find no support with Defoe's other biographers. Chalmers does not comment on the origin of *Robinson Crusoe*, Lee and Chambers both refute the allegation; and Professor Minto, the most authoritative biographer, summarizes the question in the following words: "The germ of *Robinson Crusoe*, the actual experience of Alexander Selkirk, went floating about for several years, and more than one artist dallied with it, till it finally settled and took root in the mind of the one man of his generation most capable of giving it a home and working out its artistic possibilities."[2]

However, another problem arises, as not all writers are agreed that Defoe wrote *Robinson Crusoe*. The book has been credited to Dr. John Arbuthnot, but no evidence to support this statement has been given. Lord Oxford has also been suggested as the author of *Robinson Crusoe* in two letters, the first of which was written by T. Wharton in 1774.[3] The writer states that he was informed by the Rev. Benjamin Holloway, who heard from Lord Sunderland that the first volume of *Robinson Crusoe* was written by Lord Oxford during his imprisonment in the Tower. Before attaching any significance to this letter, one is tempted to request the source of Lord Sunderland's information. Similar views were expressed by a writer signing himself "W. W."[4] in the *Gentleman's Magazine* of February 25th, 1788. This opinion seems extravagant and has not gained any subsequent favour.

A few writers believe that Defoe's *Robinson Crusoe* was not in any way connected with Selkirk's experiences. Williamson[5] raises this objection largely on geographical grounds, for, as he rightly states, Crusoe's island bears no resemblance to Juan

---

[1] G. A. AITKEN, *Romances and Narratives by Daniel Defoe*, 1895, Introduction, Vol. I, 52.

[2] WILLIAM MINTO, *Daniel Defoe*, 1879, 142.

[3] *Original Letters of Eminent Literary Men*, 1843, 320. Ed. Sir Henry Ellis.

[4] "W. W.", *Gentleman's Magazine*, 1788, 208.

[5] J. A. WILLIAMSON, *The Ocean in English History*, 1941, 164.

Fernandez and is set in a different ocean.   But Whitley states
that Defoe took pains to hide from his readers even the
slightest connection between the adventures of Robinson
Crusoe and those of Alexander Selkirk. " He began to
envelop himself in a cloud of mystery. He put back the
adventures of Robinson Crusoe many years. He placed a
whole continent between the Island of Juan Fernandez and the
Island on which Crusoe was cast away."[1]

Colonel Lesile's suggestion that Crusoe was a man of flesh
and blood, a native of York, although the son of a foreigner
of Bremen who first settled at Hull, has been refuted by
Moore.[2]   According to Aitken, there is no truth in the claims
of other castaways to be the real Robinson Crusoe.   Amongst
these was Peter Serrano who was shipwrecked on a Caribbean
island somewhat earlier than Selkirk;   Grimmelhausen's
story, *The Adventurer Simplicus Simplicimus* (1670);   and
Marivaux's account of the adventures of a castaway.   From
this brief survey of the literature, it is concluded that the
weight of authoritative opinion favours the view that Defoe's
Robinson Crusoe was in fact conceived on the basis of Selkirk's
experiences, although the relationship is only slightly evident.
Furthermore, reliable evidence of a meeting between Selkirk
and Defoe is lacking, and the story that *Robinson Crusoe* was
taken from Selkirk's papers is also unconvincing.

Neither is there a scrap of reliable evidence to support the
view that Defoe ever met Thomas Dover, although there is
some slight circumstantial evidence worthy of note.   After a
disastrous business venture in 1692 Defoe sought refuge from
his creditors in Bristol, where he was known as the " Sunday
Gentleman ", because he appeared on that day, and that day
only, in fashionable attire, being kept indoors during the rest of
the week by fear of the bailiffs.   It is not known how long
Defoe remained in Bristol, nor the date of Dover's arrival
there.   He probably resided in Bristol a few years prior to
his appointment as honorary physician at St. Peter's Hospital
in 1696.   After the voyage, Defoe, Selkirk, and Dover were

---

[1] CHARLES WHITLEY, *Introduction to Robinson Crusoe*, 1935, 16.
[2] J. R. MOORE, *Notes and Queries*, 1933, **164**, 244.

in London during the same period, but again evidence that they ever met is lacking.

Neither Dover nor Selkirk is mentioned in any of Defoe's books or newspapers. The only member of the expedition to claim his attention in print is Captain Rogers, whose name appeared in a news item of October, 1717 in *Mercurius Politicus* :[1] " Captain Rogers made Governor of the Isle of New Providence." Rogers and John Atkins (surgeon on Selkirk's last voyage) were Defoe's main sources of information for his *General History of the Pirates* published under the pseudonym of Captain Charles Johnson. As they were both acquainted with Selkirk they could also have furnished him with further information not mentioned in their books.

Defoe *might* have met anyone ; he was a tremendous traveller and news reporter. But there is no indication that he knew Dover, no indication that he knew Selkirk except through print, and perhaps oral reports from Rogers and Atkins, although it is virtually certain that he knew Rogers.

---

[1] DANIEL DEFOE, *Mercurius Politicus*, 1717, October, 747.

BIBLIOGRAPHY

MANUSCRIPTS

PUBLIC RECORDS OFFICE:
Records of the High Court of Admiralty, 1712 : Sentences (Prize), H.C.A. 34/39, No. 147.
Records of the High Court of Admiralty, 1704 : Declaration of Letters of Marque, H.C.A. 26/13, fol. 66d.
Chancery Master's Exhibits, 1712–13, C.104/36–40; 160–1. (*By kind permission of the Master in Chancery.*)
Entry Book, Chancery Decrees and Orders, 1712–13, C.33/319, *Creagh* v. *Rogers*, H.26, 30, 35, 88, 284, 414, 415, 425, 437, and 494(6). (*By kind permission of the Master in Chancery.*)
Entry Book, Chancery Decrees and Orders, 1712–13, C.33/319, ff. 130–1, *Creagh* v. *Freake*. (*By kind permission of the Master in Chancery.*)

COMMONWEALTH RELATIONS OFFICE:
(*By kind permission of the Superintendent of Records.*)
Fourteen entries in the Minutes of the Court of Directors, East India Company, from March 10, 1711, to April 26, 1712.
Miscellaneous Documents, East India Company, Vol. III. Three letters dated Aug. 24, 1711; Oct. 3, 1711; Oct. 12, 1711.

HOUSE OF LORDS:
(*By kind permission of the Clerk of Records.*)
Manuscripts of the House of Lords, 1712–14, Vol. X (New Series), No. 3136, June 17, 1714, p. 360. (Seen in proof.)
The Humble Petition of the Poor South-Sea Sailors, read in the House of Lords, Aug. 31, 1715.

BODLEIAN LIBRARY:
(*By kind permission of the Librarian.*)
MS. Top. Oxon., C.257, 1660–1737. C. M. Neale, 1917.
Rawlinson MS., B.400f., 1718.

BRITISH MUSEUM:
(*By kind permission of the Librarian.*)
Three letters from Thomas Dover to Sir Hans Sloane. *Sloane MSS.*, 4046, f. 80; 4051, f. 225; 4058, ff. 264–5.
Letter from Viscountess Dupplin to Abigail Harley. March 4, 1720. *Harley Papers*, Vol. XXXIV, f. 192a.
Letter from J. Drummond to the Earl of Oxford. August 7, 1711. *Harley Papers*, Vol. XXXIV, f. 192b.

ROYAL COLLEGE OF PHYSICIANS OF LONDON :
Eight entries in *Annals of the Royal College of Physicians of London*, Vol. VIII,
between Jan. 6, 1721, and Feb. 2, 1722. *(By kind permission of Sir Harold
Boldero.)*
MS. entitled "Medical Observations by Thomas Sydenham, London,
Martii 26, 1669 ".

PRINCIPAL PROBATE REGISTRY, SOMERSET HOUSE :
The Last Will and Testament of John Dover, proved Oct. 17, 1696.
The Last Will and Testament of the Rev. John Dover, proved Nov. 15,
1725.

MISCELLANEOUS :
The marriage settlement of Elizabeth Dover, daughter of Dr. Thomas
Dover. In the possession of Sir James Colyer-Fergusson, Bart.
"Indenture, dated 6 May, 1727, between Thomas Mander, of the Inner
Temple, Esq., and Thomas Dover, late of Barton-on-the-Heath, Co.
Warwick, now of St. Clement Dane's Parish, Co. Middlesex, doctor in
physick." *(By kind permission of the Librarian of the Royal College of
Surgeons of England.)*
Fourteen entries, between 1575 and 1760, relating to the Dover family,
in the Parish Register, Barton-on-the-Heath.
Entry of April 20, 1742, in the Parish Register of Stanway, Glos., relating
to the burial of Thomas Dover.
The Register of Admissions, Gonville and Caius College, Cambridge,
Michaelmas Term, 1686.

BOOKS AND ARTICLES

Adams, H. C., *The Original Robinson Crusoe*, 1885. London : Routledge.
Aitken, G. A., *Life and Works of John Arbuthnot*, 1892. London : Frowde.
Annalia Dubrensia (A collection by 33 contributors) *Upon the Yearly
Celebration of Mr. Robert Dover's Olimpick Games upon Cotswold Hills.*
Ed. M. Walbancke, 1636. London : Robert Raworth.
Anon., *The Antidote, or Some Remarks upon ' A Treatise on Mercury '*, 1733.
London : British Museum.
— *The Weekly Journal*, June 20, 1719.
— "Dr. Dover and His Powder ", *Med. Pr.*, 1902, **36**, 14.
Ashbee, C. R., *The Last Records of a Cotswold Community*, 1904. Gloucester-
shire Archæological Society Publication. London : Essex House Press.
Atkyns, R., *The Ancient and Present State of Glostershire*, 1712. London :
W. Bowyer & Robert Gosling.
Ayliffe, J., *The Ancient and Present State of the University of Oxford*, 1714,
Vol. II. London : E. Curll.
Barrett, W., *The History and Antiquities of the City of Bristol*, 1788. Bristol :
W. Pine.

Barton, D. P., *Links between Shakespeare and the Law*, 1928. London : Faber & Gwyer.

Beattie, J., *Dissertations Moral and Critical*, 1783. London : Strahan & Cadell.

Beazley, E. R., *Voyages and Travels mainly during the 16th and 17th Centuries*, 1903, Vol. I. London : Constable.

Belloste, A., *Hospital Surgeon*, 1695. Reprinted in 3rd ed. of *The Ancient Physician's Legacy*, 1733. London : A. Bellesworth & C. Hitch.

Benians, E. A., *Cambridge Modern History*, 1904, Vol. VI, Ch. IV. Cambridge : University Press.

Berkeley, G., *The Naval History of Britain*, 1758. London : by the author.

Bloxham, J. R., *Register of Magdalen College, Oxford*, 1776, Vol. V. London : James Parker.

Boerhaave, J. H., *Some Experiments concerning Mercury*, 1734. London : J. Roberts.

Boyes, J. H., " Dover's Powder and Robinson Crusoe ", *New Engl. J. Med.*, 1931, **204**, 440.

Bradley, H., *Physical and Philosophical Remarks on Dr. Dover's late Pamphlet*, 1733. London : C. Rimpton.

Bulleyn, W., *Bulleins Bulwarke of Defence against all sicknesse, soarenesse, and wounds that doe dayly assaulte mankinde*, 1579. London : Thos. Marshe.

Callander, J., *Terra Australis Cognita: Voyages to the Terra Australis, or Southern Hemisphere*, 1768. Edinburgh : A. Donaldson.

Castiglioni, A., *A History of Medicine*, 1947. Ed. E. B. Krumbhaar. New York : Alfred B. Knope.

Cheyne, George, *Essay on Health and Long Life*, 1st ed., 1724. London : G. Strahan and W. Mears.

Clark, A. (Ed.), *The Register of the University of Oxford*, 1889, Vol. II. Oxford Historical Society.

Comrie, J. D., *Selected Works of Thomas Sydenham*, 1922. London : John Bale.

Cooke, E., *A Voyage to the South Sea and Round the World*, 2 vols., 1712. London : R. Lintot, R. Gosling, A. Bettesworth, and W. Innys.

Country Physician, *On the Use and Abuse of Mercury, etc.*, 1733. London : British Museum.

— — *Remarks upon a late Scurilous Pamphlet entitled ' A Review of the Quicksilver Controversy', in which Dr. Turner's Character as a Great and Impartial Historian in Regard to the Same is Granted and the Author's own Impartiality, Sincerity, Falsehood and Gross Ignorance are Set Forth*, 1737. London : British Museum.

Creighton, C., *A History of Epidemics in Britain from A.D. 664 to the extinction of the Plague*, 1891, Vol. II. Cambridge : University Press.

Dampier, W., *Dampier's Voyages*, 1906, Vol. I. Ed. John Masefield. London : Grant-Richards.

Defoe, D., *Mercurius Politicus*, 1717, Oct., p. 747.

— — " Against Inoculation with Smallpox ", *The Original Weekly Journal and Saturday's Post*, 1722, April 28.

D'Israeli, I., *Curiosities of Literature*, 1824, Vol. III, p. 281. London: Thos. Davison.

Dopson, L., "Thomas Dover: Pirate and Physician", *Warw. J.*, 1947, **2**, 214.

Dover, J., *The Roman Generalls: or The Distressed Ladies*, 1667. London: Samuel Herrick.

—— *The Mall, or The Modish Lovers*, 1674. London: Wm. Cademan. (Formerly ascribed to John Dryden.)

Dover, T., *The Ancient Physician's Legacy to his Country*, 1st ed., 1732. London: A. Bellesworth & C. Hitch.

—— *The Ancient Physician's Legacy to his Country*, 1733. London. Printed for the Relict of the late R. Bradly, F.R.S.

—— *To the Author of ' The Use and Abuse of Mercury ', Ancient Physician's Legacy*, 6th ed., 1742, p. 201. London: C. Hitch, J. Brotherton, and R. Minors.

Downie, W., "Dr. Dover of Powder Fame", *Glasg. Med. J.*, 1920, **93**, 122.

Ellis, H., *Original Letters Illustrative of English History*, 1827, Vols. I, II. London: Harding & Lepard.

Eloesser, L., "Pirate and Buccaneer Doctors", *Ann. Med. Hist.*, 1926, **8**, 31.

Entick, J., *A New Naval History*, 1757. London: R. Manby.

Esquemeling, J., *The Buccaneers and Marooners of America*, Ed. Howard Pyle, 1890. London: T. Fisher Unwin.

Evans, G. (Ed.), *Medical Treatment*, 1951. London: Butterworth.

Fergusson, T. Colyer, *Notes and Queries*, "Motherhood Late in Life", 1908, 10th Series, No. 9, p. 232, and "Thomas Dover, M.B.", 1904, 10th Series, No. 11, p. 196.

Fowler, T., *History of Corpus Christi College, Oxford*, 1898. London: F. E. Robinson.

Freind, J., *Emmenologia*, 1703, p. 26.

Garrison, F. H., *An Introduction to the History of Medicine*, 4th ed., 1929. Philadelphia and London: W. B. Saunders.

Gentleman of Trinity College, Cambridge, *Encomium Argenti Vivi: A Treatise upon the Use and Properties of Quicksilver*, 1733. London: Stephen Austen.

Gentleman's Magazine, 1785, **55**, 889, 927.

Ibid., 1788, **60**, 206.

Gunther, R. T., *Early Science in Oxford*, 1925, Vols. I–IV. Oxford: University Press.

Guthrie, G., *A History of Medicine*, 1945. London: Nelson.

Hakluyt, R., *The Principal Navigations, Voyages, Traffiques and Discoveries of the English Nation*, 1905, Vols. X–XII. Glasgow: James Maclehose.

Hamilton, S. G., *Hertford College*, 1903. London: F. E. Robinson.

Harleian Miscellany, *Providence Displayed, or A Very Surprising Account of one Mr. Alexander Selkirk*, 1810, Vol. V, 402. London: John Murray.

— Society, *Visitations of Warwickshire*, 1682–3, Vol. LXII.

Harsant, W. H., " Medical Bristol in the Eighteenth Century ", *Bristol Med.-Chir. J.*, 1899, **17**, 297.

Harvey, G., *The Conclave of Physicians*, 1683. London : James Partridge.

Hone, C. R., *The Life of Dr. John Radcliffe*, 1950. London : Faber.

Howell, J., *The Life and Adventures of Alexander Selkirk, containing a real incident upon which the romance of Robinson Crusoe is founded*, 1825. Edinburgh : Oliver.

Howell, T. H., " Dover's Legacy ", *Edinb. Med. J.*, 1942, **49**, 266.

Hume, D., *History of England*, 1797, Vol. VI. London : T. Cadell.

Hydrargyrum, *Substantial Reasons Offer'd by Way of Argument to prove that Crude Mercury never did, nor can hurt any one taking it. Being the Greatest Discovery that was ever made to Mankind*, 1733. London : British Museum.

Hyett, F. A., " Annalia Dubrensia", *Trans. Bristol and Glouc. Archæological Soc.*, 1923, **45**, 153.

Jeaffreson, J. C., *A Book about Doctors*, 1860. London : Hurst & Black.

Jewell, N. P., and Kauntze, W. H., *Handbook of Tropical Fevers*, 1932. London : Baillière, Tindall & Cox.

Johnson, J., *Transactions of the Corporation of the Poor in the City of Bristol*, 1826. Bristol : P. Rose.

Krantz, J. C., and Carr, C. J., *Pharmacologic Principles of Medical Practice*, 2nd ed., 1951. Baltimore : Williams & Wilkins.

Latimer, J., *Annals of Bristol in the 17th Century*, 1900. Bristol : William George's Sons.

— — *Annals of Bristol in the 18th Century*, 1893. Bristol : Printed for the Author.

Lecky, W. E. H., *A History of England in the 18th Century*, 1878, Vol. I. London : Longmans, Green.

Lesile, R. C., *Life Aboard a British Privateer in the Time of Queen Anne*, 1889. London : Chapman & Hall.

MacArthur, W. P., " Malaria in England ", *Brit. Med. Bull.*, 1951, **8**, 76.

Mackay, C., *Memoirs of Extraordinary Popular Delusions*, 1841, Vol. 1, 74. London : Richard Bentley.

MacMichael, W., *The Gold-Headed Cane*, 1953. Springfield, Ill. : C. C. Thomas.

Mallet, C. E., *A History of the University of Oxford*, 1924, Vols. II, III. London : Methuen.

Martindale, *Extra Pharmacopœia*, 23rd ed., 1952. London : Pharmaceutical Press.

Mead, R., *A Short Discourse Concerning Pestilential Contagion and Methods to be used to Prevent it*, 4th ed., 1720. London : Sam Buckley and Ralph Smith.

— — *A Treatise concerning the Influence of the Sun and Moon upon Human Bodies*, 1748, trans. T. Stack. London : Sam Buckley and Ralph Smith.

Mercurialist, *A Short Review of the Quicksilver Controversy*, 1733. London : British Museum.

Minto, W., *Daniel Defoe*, 1879. London : Macmillan.

Monro, T. K., *The Physician as Man of Letters, Science and Action*, 2nd ed., 1951. Edinburgh : Livingstone.

Moore, J. P., " Defoe, Robin and Crusoe", *Notes and Queries*, 1933, **164**, 26.

— — " Defoe, Selkirk and John Atkins", *Ibid.*, 1940, **179**, 436.

Moore, N., *Dictionary of National Biography*, 1888, Vol. XV, p. 382. London : Smith, Elder.

Munk, W., *The Roll of the Royal College of Physicians of London*, 2nd ed., 1878, Vol. II, p. 79.

Nias, J. B., *Dr. John Radcliffe*, 1918. Oxford : Clarendon Press.

Nichols, J., *Literary Anecdotes of the 18th Century*, 1812, Vol. I, p. 534. London : Nichols & Bentley.

Nixon, J. A., " Thomas Dover, Physician and Merchant Adventurer ", *Bristol Med.-Chir. J.*, 1909, **27**, 31.

— — " Further Notes on Thomas Dover ", *Proc. R. Soc. Med.*, Sect. Hist., 1912–13, **6**, 233.

— — " Thomas Dover, Physician and Circumnavigator ", *Brit. med. J.*, 1913, **1**, 619.

— — " Salt-water Surgeons ", *Lancet*, 1941, **2**, 774.

Orr-Ewing, H. J., " Medicine in Eighteenth-century Bristol ", *Bristol Med.-Chir. J.*, 1950, **67**, 6.

Osler, W., " Thomas Dover, Physician and Buccaneer ", *Johns Hopk. Hosp. Bull.*, 1896, **7**, 1.

— — *The Evolution of Modern Medicine*, 1921. New Haven : Yale University Press.

Parker, G., " Medical Organisation and the Growth of the Medical Sciences in the Seventeenth Century, illustrated by the Lives of the Local Worthies ", *Bristol Med.-Chir. J.*, 1911, **29**, 6.

— — "The Allegory of Robinson Crusoe ", *History*, 1925, **10**, 11.

Payne, J. F., *Thomas Sydenham*, 1900. London : T. Fisher Unwin.

Pharmacopœia Radcliffeana, 2nd ed., 1716. London : Charles Rivington.

Phear, D. N., " Thomas Dover, 1662–1742 ", *J. Hist. Med.*, 1954, **9**, 139.

Powell, J. W. D., *Bristol Privateers and Ships of War*, 1930. Bristol : Arrowsmith.

Power, D'Arcy, *Selected Writings*, 1877–1930, **1931**. Oxford : University Press.

Riddell, W. R., " Dr. Thomas Dover and his Legacy ", *Med. J. Rec.*, 1930, **132**, 90.

Riesman, D., *Thomas Sydenham*, 1926. New York : Paul B. Hoeber.

Rogers, B. M. H., " Woodes Rogers' Privateering Voyage, 1708–11 ", *Mariners Mirror*, 1933, **14**, 208.

Rogers, Woodes, *A Cruising Voyage round the World*, 1st ed., 1712. London : A. Bell.

— — *A Cruising Voyage round the World*, with Introduction by G. E. Manwaring, 1928. London : Cassell.

Rolleston, H., " Irregular Practice and Quackery ", *Canad. med. Ass. J.*, 1927, **17**, 501.

Rudder, S., *A New History of Gloucestershire*, 1779. Cirencester : Printed by the author.

Rudge, T., *History of Gloucestershire*, 2 vols., 1804. London : Longmans.

Russell, M. P., " Thomas Dover 1660–1742 ", *Edinb. med. J.*, 1942, **49**, 259.

Salzman, L. F. (Ed.), *A History of the County of Warwick*. Victoria County History Series, 1949. Oxford : University Press.

Sinclair, H. M., and Robb-Smith, A. H. T., *A Short History of Anatomical Teaching in Oxford*, 1950. Oxford : University Press.

Singer, C., *A Short History of Medicine*, 1928. Oxford : University Press.

Skirving, R. S., " Two Sea-faring Doctors of the Past ", *Med. J. Aust.*, 1924, **I**, 358.

Smollett, T., *An Essay on the External Use of Water, etc.*, 1752. London : M. Cooper. Bath : Leake & Frederick.

Spence, J., *Anecdotes, Observations and Characters of Books and Men*, 1858. Ed. S. W. Singer. London : J. B. Smith.

Stark, F. R., *The Abolition of Privateering and Declaration of Paris*, 1897. Vol. VIII. New York.

Steele, R., *The Englishmen*, 1713, Dec. 3, No. 26 ; cf. " The Englishman ", Ed. R. Blanchard, 1955, p. 106. Oxford : Clarendon Press.

— — *The Antidote, in a letter to a Free Thinker, occasion'd by the Dispute between Dr. Woodward and certain other Physicians*, 1719. London : J. Roberts.

— — *The Antidote No. 2, occasion'd by Later Actions between Dr. Woodward and Dr. Mead*, 1719. London : J. Roberts.

Strype, J., *Life of Archbishop Grindal*, 1821. Oxford : Clarendon Press.

Sutherland, L. S., *The East India Company in 18th Century Politics*, 1952. Oxford : University Press.

Swann, J. (Ed.), *The Entire Works of Dr. Thomas Sydenham*, 3rd ed., 1753. London : E. Cave.

Traill, H. D., and Man, J. S., *Social England*, 1895, Vols. IV, V. London : Cassell.

Trevelyan, G. M., *English Social History*, 1944. London : Longmans, Green.

Tuberville, A. S. (Ed.), *Johnson's England*, 1933, Vol. II. Oxford : Clarendon Press.

Turner, Daniel, *The Ancient Physician's Legacy, impartially survey'd and his Practice prov'd Repugnant, etc.*, 1733. London : John Clarke.

Venn, J., " Academic Sports, A Buccaneering Physician ", *The Caian*, 1912, **17**, 32.

— — *Biographical History of Gonville and Caius College*, 1897, Vol. I, p. 481. Cambridge : University Press.

— — *Early Collegiate Life*, 1913. Cambridge : Heffer.

— — *Caius College*, 1923. Cambridge : University Press.

Whitley, C., Introduction to *Robinson Crusoe*, 1935. London : Constable.

Whitten, W., *Daniel Defoe*, 1900. London : K. Paul.

Williamson, J. A., *The Ocean in English History*, 1941. Oxford : Clarendon Press.

Wilson, W., *Memoirs of the Life and Times of Daniel De Foe*, 1830, Vol. III. London : Hurst & Chance.

Winslow, F. B., *Physic and Physicians*, 2 vols., 1842.   London : Henry Renshaw.

Wood, Anthony, *The History and Antiquities of the University of Oxford*, 2 vols., 1796.   Trans. and ed. John Gutch.   Oxford : Printed for the Editor.

— — *Athenae Oxonienses*, 3rd ed., 1813, Vols. I–IV.   Ed. Philip Bliss. London : F. C. & J. Rivington.

Wootton, A. C., *Chronicles of Pharmacy*, 2 vols., 1910.   London : Macmillan.

Wordsworth, C., *Social Life at the English Universities in the 18th Century*, 1874.   Cambridge : Deighton, Bell.

Wright, T., *The Life of Daniel Defoe*, 1894.   London : Cassell.

INDEX